Guns and Magnolias

Elfreida Read

ISBN 0 88750 773 5 (hardcover)
ISBN 0 88750 774 3 (softcover)

Book design by Michael Macklem

Printed in Canada

PUBLISHED IN CANADA BY OBERON PRESS

To my dear husband, who has never lost touch with the magnolias.

Chapter One

We first heard the guns in late August, 1937, when we were playing tennis on the Race Course, the giant outdoor recreation centre in the heart of the Shanghai International Settlement. We thought the sound we heard was thunder.

For me it was the summer of the swains.

A year had passed since my idyllic vacation in North China, in Peitaiho and Peking. I had changed. The change was radical, although, in the way of all growth changes, it had been unobtrusive, so that I had been unaware of the process. My sixteen-year-old body had started to fill out, those scrawny elbows and knees underwent a magical transformation. My legs were now long and svelte, and brown from daily exposure on sun-drenched tennis courts. I altered my hairstyle to conform to the trend of the day, a topknot of rolled curls and a pageboy bob, a style into which my strange hair slipped easily, with no frizzy ends apparent. I was still not allowed to wear makeup, but to my immense gratitude my sister, though she did not rise to lipstick, did come through with a small box of rouge, making me promise never to let Mother see me with the rouge on my face. I kept it in my purse, a little round brown box, surely the ticket to success. I applied the rouge only when I was well away from home, removing it before returning. These changes wrought an astonishing revolution in my life. The boys I had met at my confirmation class and whom I continued to meet Sunday after Sunday at the Anglican Cathedral, suddenly became attentive.

The change in me was not confined to my appearance. I had also started to move away from my childhood associations. In the emigrant home in which I had grown up, the home my Estonian parents had created for me and my sister after the catastrophe of the Russian Revolution, I had always been surrounded by Russian emigrant friends and relatives,

5

and in my English public school that comprised a variety of nationalities, I had naturally gravitated to children with similar backgrounds, but since my confirmation in the Anglican Cathedral, which event had been brought about by pressure from my elders and my curious interpretation of the ways of God, my emigrant ambience began to oppress me.

The male confirmees in my church class, in the grey flannels and purple blazers distinctive of the exclusive English Cathedral School, had brought a totally novel excitement into my life. I had never known any boys of my own age before. And I also began to consider for possible friendship the English girls I met at the church.

This was by no means simple. In a community as class conscious as the International Settlement of Shanghai, in the year 1937, emigrants and British did not mix easily.

The British were at the top of the heap. It was an accepted circumstance—as a classmate had once said to me, "The British don't have to be good at anything, they just need to be British." So there they were at the top with a number of not quite so visible but equally weighty Americans, and just under them came the French and the Germans and the Scandinavians. Below these, and slightly suspect, were the Greeks and Italians and a sprinkling of central Europeans. Considerably lower on the scale we had the Japanese, though there were few at that time, and they were closely followed by the jetsam and flotsam of society, the Jews, the emigrant Russians, the Eurasians and, last of all, the Chinese. There were also the Sikhs who seemed to be nearly all policemen and were in a class by themselves, for, in spite of being British, they were dark-skinned and therefore totally unacceptable in our eyes.

These divisions were not always based on wealth. There were extremely rich Jews and Eurasians and Chinese, but the stigma of the racial differentiations clung fast. These racial categories were never specifically mentioned, but they were as much with us as the weather. We knew exactly where

6

everyone fitted in and we went through a mental gradation exercise every time we met a new person. My parents, being Estonian and therefore floating in a kind of no-man's land, would never have countenanced my marrying a Jew or a Eurasian, a Sikh or a Japanese, and the Chinese, of course, were totally beyond the pale. So deeply internalized was the delineation between Chinese and white that I grew up with absolutely no sexual inclinations whatsoever toward Chinese males. I hardly thought of the Chinese as having any private lives at all—that they had joys, sorrows, abilities, ambitions, desires, or, in the last extremity, a sex life, never entered my consideration. Until my immersion in the marvels of Peking and the grandeur of the Chinese past, I perceived them as a breed of automatons, somehow there for my convenience.

So with the British at the top of the heap and the Russian emigrants bumping the bottom, I could see that my emigrant associations would be a distinct disadvantage in the swing my life had taken toward the British community. It never occurred to me to question the presence of those authoritarian persons in someone else's land or their assumption of hegemony. I saw no weaknesses in the structure of the life they had created for themselves, no threat. I saw only their homes and their possessions, I saw their warships in the harbour. Their language predominated in the Settlement. I envied their ascendancy. So in order to fall in with this attractive group I could not afford to be too different. I had to disassociate myself as much as possible from my Russian connections.

I fell back on my Estonian nationality. Estonians were closer to Scandinavians I reasoned. That brought me well up on the racial scale. I began to stress my Estonian ancestry. I was *Estonian* I told my new friends. Estonians were not Russians. Yes, we were living in Russia at the time of the revolution, but that no more made me Russian than living in China made them Chinese. A trump card.

7

It made sense to me at a time when sense was not para-
mount in the formation of my conclusions. But I was
plagued with guilt and misery, for my emigrant family
presented certain elements of profound embarrassment.

I did not mind my new friends meeting my father.
Although he retained a faint Germanic accent, his English
was flawless and his erudition unimpeachable. My sister,
educated in an English school and married to a New Zea-
lander, was a great asset as was her handsome husband, but
alas, my poor mother was a disaster. Her pretty looks, her
quick wit, her kindness, did nothing to compensate for her
broken English. I loved her so dearly but in the estimation
of my new friends no-one but a discounted Russian emigrant
mangled English like that. If I chanced to meet one of my
fancy friends when I was out with her I agonized, a mixture
of resentment and protectiveness swirling around my heart.
That she fluently spoke two other languages to their only
one carried no weight.

My jolly Uncle Ernest and his wife, the passionate and
disturbed Maria Mikhailovna, were on the border line of my
list of doubtful connections. After my mother's declaration
of independence when she had issued an ultimatum to Uncle
Ernest and Maria Mikhailovna, occasioning the Great Rift,
they had moved out of the house we had been sharing on
Victory Terrace, but time had healed the rift and we were
now on friendly terms again. Meeting one of them when in
the company of my fine new companions was a constant
threat. They both spoke good enough English and I could
talk about my Uncle Ernest's job with the Shanghai Power
Company, one of the most prestigious American firms in the
city, and Maria Mikhailovna's eccentricity was acceptable
for I could make much of her touted wealth (without men-
tioning its loss), but there was always the chance that they
might address me in Russian, and my Uncle Ernest was fond
of teasing, which was exasperating. However my anxiety
with regard to them was minimal compared to the grief and

8

confusion I suffered on account of my doctor uncle, my beloved Aunt Lena, my kindly Aunt Lida, so recently brought out of Russia with her store of tales of The Terror, and my dear cousin Nina, the patient and generous playmate of my earlier years. It had never even entered my mind prior to this turn in my life that I could possibly ever be embarrassed by them. But embarrassed I was.

Nina presented the least problem. She was beautiful and rich, for my doctor uncle had done well in the Shanghai community. She was always sought after, and of course spoke impeccable English. But she did go to that strange Russian Orthodox church, and her life was closely interwoven with that of the Russian emigrants in the city. My aunt and uncle had many charitable projects, among them the orphanage for young victims of the revolution, the Russian Hospital where the doctor treated impecunious emigrants free of charge and the Russian Orthodox Church that also benefited from his generosity, but these worthy projects cut no ice in my new circles and were in fact curiously damaging. I did take some pride in revealing that my uncle was a doctor, respected and much in demand, but alas, the doctor too spoke broken English, although not as broken as my mother's and Aunt Lena's, to say nothing of poor Aunt Lida, whose English was in shards.

My old schoolfriend of so many years standing, my partner in tennis glories and my reading companion, Olga Sokoloff, was another casualty of my lately assumed and ill-founded affectations. Although I had not lost my fondness for Olga, and indeed I never lost that, I felt ill at ease introducing her to my new friends. Deserving as she was of affection and loyalty, she did not, nonetheless, belong to the Cathedral, she did not fit into the group to which I was so attracted.

As for my home, it was a major calamity. Not one of my recently acquired friends lived in a terrace house. I had always hated Victory Terrace ever since we had moved into it when I was twelve at the instigation of my Uncle Ernest and his wife Maria Mikhailovna. We had shared the ugly, gaunt house with them for over two years, until Maria Mikhailovna's compulsive nature and her passion for dogs had brought about the Great Rift. The house, narrow and ill-designed, rose to a height of six floors with a room appendaged to each flight of interminable stairs and its gloom and its vertiginous ascents filled my young soul with the deepest resentment against the architects of the monstrosity, against my uncle and his wife, and against my parents who had agreed to move into it. The young people with whom I now consorted, lived in detached two-storeyed homes set in spacious grounds reached by way of shady, leafy-treed avenues. We reached our home by way of a glaring, treeless cement lane at the entrance of which a giant open garbage container attracted flies and itinerant beggar children, and old Chinese women searching for salvable food and rubbish. When I went to Grace Arlington's house my heart shrank at the thought of inviting her to mine.

Grace's parents were among those well-placed, solidly entrenched, excellently outfitted, fed and housed pillars of the community, primarily British but including, too, nationals of other privileged countries, who lived the true colonial life secluded in one of those gracious homes, attended by servants as saints are attended by angels in pictures of heaven. These were people who never felt out of place in someone else's land. The Settlement was simply an extension of their own homeland, their position of dominance represented an arm of their sovereign state. They had no doubt whatsoever of their superiority and at that time I believed in it too. I think I believed in it far more than Grace Arlington ever did. I suspect she simply took her status for granted and shrugged it off. She was an unassuming, pleasant young person in a situation thrust upon her by circumstances. But I read more into it than that. Grace had become my friend after the confirmation, but the friendship, warm on her side, was wary on mine.

What was I to do then, beset by so many impediments wrought so grievously by fate? In the company of my new friends I avoided mention of my parents, of my dreadful home (we even *rented out* a room, which appalling fact could never, never be revealed), of my Russian emigrant connections. I met them at the church, and in the summer at the Race Course, where I joined the exclusive Cathedral Tennis Club on the basis of my membership at the Anglican Cathedral. I was vague when asked where I lived, I never invited anyone to visit me. I said my father was a savant who spoke many languages and didn't like to be disturbed when he was busy with his books, which wasn't so far from the truth, and that my mother sacrificed her life to protecting him from the intrusions of the outside world. I wove an air of mystery around myself, based on erudition and my own brand of exclusiveness, and the young people, most of whom were as silly as I was, swallowed it.

I was totally unaware of how far I had grown away from that little girl who kept her family of beloved dolls seated in rows on a black wickerwork trunk that had travelled all the way with her from Russia, the little girl who had shed tears when she had been told that the day was coming when she would no longer be playing with dolls. I was unaware of how far I had grown away even from the teenager of only a year ago who had fantasized about sheikhs, counted falling stars, dreamed about the Gobi Desert and had been awestruck by the marvels of China's magnificent past. The self-absorbed, evasive, manipulative young person I had become was somebody new, and those previous others, hidden deep within my psyche, watched in wonder and some sadness, waiting for a chance to reinstate their claims.

At the Anglican Cathedral, situated in the heart of downtown Shanghai, there were early-morning communion services on Sundays, followed by large and rowdy church-hall breakfasts for which all the lately confirmed boys and girls turned up. I soon realized that piety had no hand in these gatherings, that the boys and girls came only to meet one another on neutral ground. All through the winter and spring of 1936 / 7 I went to church and eyed the boys from a safe distance. Just before Christmas I sat for the Senior Cambridge University Entrance Examinations and in the spring, with studies well behind me, I gave my undivided attention to this exhilarating sphere of interest. Soon I found that the safe distance was narrowing. To my amazement and gratification I found the boys were closing in.

At first they manoeuvred in a group. I found this group sitting opposite Grace Arlington and me at the breakfasts after the early-morning communion services. I found them strolling to the 10.30 service that Grace and I attended without fail, albeit with little regard for devoutness. The saints looked down censoriously from the stained-glass windows, Jesus and his apostles turned martyred faces upon us, but our thoughts were as far removed from them as was our place in time. A sweet intoxicating wine had replaced the blood in our veins. Although our eyes were fixed on the stalwart figure of the Dean in his grand vestments we were oblivious of the service, but we were aware of every move in the pew to our right, where the swains invariably seated themselves. We were as taut as tightrope artists.

Outside, the spring was drunken with magnolia blossoms, the sky blue and everlasting. Life rolled away ahead of us in vast entrancing waves as we walked out of the church to the pealing of the great bells in the belfry, an ocean of enchantment, a delirium of possibilities. One Sunday we found that somehow we and the swains were all sitting in the same pew.

There were three of them, great foolish louts who walked with a rolling gait, trendy at the time. They took us to movies, to the Jessfield Park with the zoo notorious for its stench and a donkey that ate paper bags and for strolls along the famous Shanghai Bund. There the great houses of -com merce, the banks and the hotels, and the consulates with their proud flags, formed an impressive skyline, and from the Bund Gardens the whole panorama of the Whangpoo River as it moved sluggishly to mix its waters with the mighty Yangtze lay before us. We watched the junks with their patched sails and the sampans and river barges that brought in fresh produce from the hinterland and we stared in awe at the great foreign ships, representing all the sea-going nations in the world, and supplying the port with every conceivable kind of merchandise. Steeped in a novel sensuousness we leaned on the rails along the embankment, elbows touching, and listened to the riverport sounds of loading and unloading, to the creaky winches and pulleys, the crashing of crates, the shouts of the foremen and the eternal chanting of the sweaty, bare-backed coolies, the chanting that ate into our hearts to remain there forever.

Though we asked other girls to join us I recognized a subtle ploy on the part of each swain to gain my undivided attention. It was heady. I could never choose among the three of them, although one, a truly classical clown with charmingly haphazard teeth and a ridiculous cavalier attitude, asserted a kind of main-man possessiveness. I was in love with all of them and none of them, and most of all I was in love with my own youth. Or perhaps I had suddenly discovered a replacement for the beloved dolls of my childhood.

I launched into the gayest, most carefree summer of my life. The swains all belonged to the Cathedral Tennis Club and that summer of 1937 we hung around there from noon till dark. The tennis club was one of many that sprang up every May on the Shanghai Race Course, complete with bamboo and grass-mat clubhouse, dark blue screens, weed-free courts, clubhouse servants and small Chinese ball boys, and disappeared as if by magic at the end of September. I played tennis constantly, and I worked hard at it. I came down before anyone else and practised with the Chinese pro, the marker, and my game improved beyond all my hopes. There was always a lighthearted rivalry among the swains as to who should partner me in the mixed doubles, and sometimes I let them draw lots. I assured them that I loved them all, and it was true. It was a sweet, innocent comradeship in which I revelled. Apart from my constant fear of intrusion from one or another of my embarrassing relatives, it was an inebriating summer.

My brain seemed to have taken a holiday. I neglected Olga who had joined the Russian Tennis Club, also on the Race Course but not in such a prime location as ours. My cousin, Nina, and her parents had left for Kuling, a mountain resort up the Yangtze River, on their summer holidays and I gave no thought to them. I avoided any claims made upon me by my family.

My memorable vacation of the previous summer to Peitaiho and Peking had awakened me to the grandeur of the Chinese past. On the train back to Shanghai I had vowed to find out more about the people in whose land we had made our home, the people who had given us asylum from the revolution in Russia when we needed it and and asked nothing in return. I had promised myself to spend more time with my father and his inexhaustible store of knowledge to acquaint myself with the events that were taking place in the hinterland of China, events to which I had been paying scant attention. I did not keep these vows. I hardly ever read the paper, I never listened to news on the radio. I heard my parents talking about "disturbances" and "troubles" and quite often someone would mention communists. Usually those conversations would end on an upbeat, optimistic note— "Don't worry, Chiang Kai-shek will fix them," someone would say. Except that the Japanese had occupied some distant northern, almost mythical, place called Manchuria and renamed it Manchukuo, I knew nothing of the immense convulsions crippling the vast country where I was spending the carefree days of my youth. The summer before in

Peitaiho, we had eaten mangoes on the beach, ridden donkeys to the sand dunes, watched for shooting stars, as if nothing else in the world existed.

And when I returned, instead of seeking the information I had thought so desirable, I plunged into my absorbing new interests relegating my intended studies of the Chinese historical scene to some later time, some time less charged with glamour and romance and sheer delight in living, although I could not imagine that such a time would ever come. My sudden and successful association with the opposite sex seemed to have knocked the last vestiges of sense out of my head. I was filled with a kind of joyful lunacy, a sense of removal from all responsibility. I was the queen-bee and answerable to no-one. The Spanish Civil War was passing me by, the activities of the Third Reich meant nothing to me. I knew that there was a steady influx of German Jews into the city but the reasons for this were very hazy in my head. Their migration did not arouse any sense of foreboding in me. The constant talk of communists and the Japanese presence in China was merely tedious.

And so the shock of awakening to the real world was probably worse for me than for those who had been following the happenings of the past years. But even for them the sudden turn of events in August of 1937 was unheralded and traumatic.

I was playing tennis on the Race Course at my fancy club, a mixed doubles match that could take my swain with the haphazard teeth and me into the finals. He had won the toss when we first heard the distant rumbles. We looked up. The relentless blue of a typical Shanghai summer sky stretched from horizon to horizon. "Thunder?" someone asked dubiously. "Must be far away, not a cloud in sight," someone else said. But what else could it be? We went on playing and the rumbles continued spasmodically, broken now by sharper, crackling volleys.

"Hold it," said the umpire. Someone was shouting from

15

the clubhouse. I did not know it, but the rumblings, the staccato echoes bouncing off the metallic skies, the commotion in the clubhouse, signalled the end of my blissful adolescence.

Someone had a radio. The Japanese had executed a surprise landing on the banks of the Whangpoo River, close to where it joined the Yantgze. It was their big naval guns we were hearing, and the scattering of machine-gun fire.

"We'd better close up," the club manager said. "All you kids had best get along home."

We didn't want to go. We couldn't believe it was true. And in any case the Japanese would never dare to attack the *Settlement*. The sacred, inviolable Settlement. The *British* Settlement as it was often called.

But we were told to go, our match unplayed. The Chinese ballboys set about letting down the nets for the night and the servants began to clear the deck of the clubhouse. My main swain and I were having a last drink of lemonade when one of those white-robed servants whisked the table away from under our glasses to stack at the back of the shed. His usually cheerful face was drawn. The Chinese were terrified of the Japanese and with good reason. The cruelty of the Japanese military was legendary.

We drank the lemonade standing up and my swain suddenly seemed very dear to me. With the prescience of disaster hanging over us, they all seemed indescribably dear, the boys and girls of my carefree summer, and the bond of our association was all at once highlighted, as by a nimbus, made almost unendurably poignant. The moment passed. We changed, and left for our buses.

At home there was a sense of restrained panic. My parents repeatedly reassured each other of the inviolability of the Settlement. On the radio we listened to Carroll Allcott, on station RUOK, telling us the news blow by blow. The Japanese were firing at Chinese entrenchments in the northeastern section of the city, the east end of my childhood. Their flagship, the "Idzuma," was on the river by the Japanese Consulate close to the Bund. The Chinese were trying to sink the "Idzuma." We were all to stay at home. No-one was to go downtown. All the offices would be shut.

"War," my father said, a note of the deepest despondency in his voice. "War. Again."

We heard that refugees from the surrounding Chinese cities were pouring into the Settlement for protection. These cities were already on fire, the blaze was spreading fast. The Settlement authorities were trying to keep the refugees out, there was no place for the thousands that sought shelter. They were coming in droves, their belongings piled on carts and waggons, wheelbarrows and rickshaws. The Shanghai Volunteer Corps had been mobilized for the protection of the Settlement.

I had a phone call from my main swain. He had been called, he said. He was in the Transport Division. I wished him luck. My sister phoned to tell us that Jack, her husband, had been called too. He was in the Signals Corps. She sounded desolate and desolation spread over me as well. It was finally beginning to seep through into my unwilling, rejecting brain that my carefree days were over, that I was no longer queen-bee, that events of greater importance than my romantic whirl had overwhelmed us, and that my distress was minimal compared to what was going on all around me.

Chapter Two

In the computerized eighties, on our backyard patio in Vancouver, surrounded by trees and a profusion of flowers, I sit drinking tea with my 93-year-old aunt. She has come to visit. The patio table and chairs and the large brown umbrella stand under a birch tree. The tree nestles its lower branches lovingly around the umbrella. Quiet envelops us. Time holds its breath as if in deference to my aunt's age and endurance. She has seen so much, lived through so many changes. Although she is tiny, and fragile as Dresden china, she is still somehow commanding, a person to be reckoned with. I think back to the days when my aunt seemed tall to me, truly authoritative then, when I skipped along beside her in my short navy uniform, my head reaching only to her shoulder as she shepherded me home from my faraway school, giving my mother an occasional much-needed break; the days when she was the purveyor of candy, English toffees, butterscotch and nougat, and my favourite, condensed milk, and Sunkist oranges when I was ill. I think of my aunt when she held her disapproval of my Uncle Ernest's marriage to the enigmatic Maria Mikhailovna, divorcée and prodigal, and senior to my uncle by nearly a decade, like a pair of giant shears over the family lines of connectedness. She never used those shears, but the threat of her disapproval was awesome, rooted as it was in her unimpeachable integrity. This integrity has never faltered. I would entrust my aunt with my life.

We talk, as always, in Russian, and our conversation proceeds something along these lines:

"We're lucky to be living in Vancouver," she says. "It's so beautiful. We should be so grateful."

I nod agreement. We emigrated from China upon the Communist takeover so many years ago to come to this gracious city and, yes, we have been lucky. But something tugs at me, something I can't quite define. My aunt puts it into words for me.

"Yet Shanghai is still somehow closer to my heart," she says.

Recently I received a letter from my British husband's sister who had left the Far East in her early twenties to settle in England. She hated the weather, she said, longed for the sun. "I still miss the Far East," she wrote, "I suppose I have never really felt I belonged here." England was the land of her forefathers but China had captured her heart never to let it go.

My aunt looks around the garden, the weed-free lawn, the sun-rich colours of the flowers endlessly flowing in the light breeze. "Of course," she adds, "it was never as peaceful as this. We had our ups and down with those Chinese always fighting. But we were young then." She sighs. "Oh, and it was good! The food—you can't buy food like that here—do you remember the Café Federal, with all those cakes? And the clothes and the servants, the holidays, the ships ..." She takes a little sip of tea and shakes her head. The sun glances off the silvery grey of her neat wig. "Always the communists," she says, "always the communists spoiling everything."

"China was a shambles," I remind her. "The government was full of crooks, the peasants were starving. The peasants were starving in Russia too when the Bolsheviks took over," I add daringly. She doesn't like to be reminded of that although I know she's thinking of that first migration too, the migration of the White Russians streaming out of their native land, and she among them with her youthful Russian doctor husband, fleeing the rage of the revolutionaries. But she always insists that reforms, extensive reforms, had been on the books before the First World War. It was the war that gave the push to the revolution, she says. The Bolsheviks took advantage of an exhausted government, a Tsar at the end of his endurance.

She cocks her head thoughtfully. "We're all allotted our place in life," she says. "God and fate make the allotments. We don't know why some turn out rich and some poor."

"That isn't going to satisfy the poor," I parry. "Maybe not," she says, her mouth puckering enigmatically, "but maybe it's God's way of trying to teach us to help one another. Who knows?" She shrugs. "I can't say it's been too successful," she adds impishly. She's a firm believer in fate. "It's fate," she will say at the news of some misfortune. "What can you do? It's fate." "God and nature," she often says, shaking her head censoriously. "I'd have done it differently." And she would have, this delicate Dresden lady with a Titan's heart. Did she not overcome a tyrannical father to become a nurse at a time when professional women were scorned as mavericks?

"Do you remember our holiday in Peitaiho and Peking?" she asks a trifle wistfully.

"Of course," I say. How could I forget it? That holiday signalled the end of my childhood, signalled the end of what I imagined to be the eternal order of things. Everything began to change after Peitaiho, after Peking.

"We never paid enough attention to what was going on in China," she says. "I don't think we wanted to know. We didn't want another war, another revolution. We had found a haven."

When she finishes her tea I offer to drive her home, but she refuses. She doesn't have far to walk, she says, the old independence bridling. I see her out of the front door and return to the patio. It isn't quite time to start dinner, I can reminisce a little. The birch tree murmurs above me. It will not be wholly mine until I'm forced to part from it. Nothing is wholly nor certainly ours until we lose it. Like Shanghai. It is now completely ours, the Old Shanghai, hers and mine, to remember as we will, to turn over in our hands and shake and see the memories falling like the snow in glass paperweights.

Looking back I find it hard to believe just how ignorant I was of what was happening in China at that time.

I heard a lot of talk about communists. Everyone seemed to be obsessed by communists and nobody had a good word for them. I heard that the revolutionary soldiers, hungry and badly equipped, swarmed through the villages robbing and killing. Ah Foh, our Chinese servant, told us about these.

They were murderers, bandits, Chinese versions of the dreaded Russian Bolsheviks. The word Bolshevik in my mind had always been evocative of fierce and evil men armed with knives and pistols, always on the warpath. It wasn't till I was in my late teens that I discovered the word Bolshevik meant simply someone who belonged to the "bolshoi" or "large" political party.

Once in a while a lone voice, usually my father's, was raised questioning the ruling government of China. How was it possible that millions could die of famine and nothing was done? Why were the Chinese so primitive? Had opium, introduced into China by the British and backed by their guns, undermined the vitality of the Chinese people? Did not conditions like that invite revolution? But such a lone questioner was quickly and fiercely quashed, his tentative wonderings out-voiced by the champions of the status quo of the day. Chief among these were the profit-seekers, milking China of her resources, but curiously supportive of these entrepreneurs, although at the other end of the financial spectrum, were the Russian emigrants who had been stripped of their own possessions and to whom revolution was anathema. They failed to see in China's travail the same conditions for revolution as had prevailed in Russia. In their eyes the peasants who had perpetrated the uprisings in Russia had been whipped up by the Bolsheviks to a fury they themselves would never have engendered. The peasants had been pawns in the game of evil sophisticates.

This was the tenacious belief of the Russian emigrants among whom we lived and who were our friends, and who daily prayed for the re-instatement of a Tsar in Russia. The belief was founded in dispossession, in suffering, in humiliation. It was hard to fault, impossible to confront and challenge.

I grew up with the Tsar in the family, as if he were yet another uncle. I knew all about him, how kind he was, how gracious, how noble. I knew about the palaces where he and his family spent their winters and their summers, about the beautiful daughters and the sickly son and about the anxiety-crazed empress and her fanatic advisor, Rasputin. I knew about the unpardonable murder of the hapless royal family at Ekaterinburg. I was revolted by the tale. It was the work of the Bolsheviks.

It was only in my late teens when I had been reading widely and obsessively for a few years, and found time to listen to my father, that I began to find out other things about Russia. I discovered that there had been famines in Russia too, that there had been primitive and incredibly poor people, that the Tsar and his government had ignored them, that unarmed petitioners to the Tsar had been mercilessly gunned down in front of one of those fine palaces. I learned that almost ninety percent of all Russians were illiterate at the time of the revolution and that the Russian Orthodox Church had conspired to keep the peasants ignorant, superstitious and poor to ensure its own supremacy. But in my middle teens I knew none of this.

Thus, knowing nothing, I was able to draw no disquieting comparisons. To me the hinterland of China was a vast, quiet expanse of fields broken by occasional villages of grey houses with black curved roofs, water buffalo and waterwheels, slime-covered creeks, wheelbarrows, chickens, wild dogs and the odour of the "honey" carts carrying raw sewage for the fertilization of the fields. There were also grave mounds, and picturesque willow trees, and once in a while upon a distant hill, a pagoda, breath-stopping in its beauty. I knew that white missionaries travelled among the Chinese preaching the teachings of Jesus and giving medical aid. Altogether an unthreatening enough picture.

That there were rivers, long, polluted and world famous for periodically flooding and drowning millions and ruining crops and homesteads, that more millions died of famines and disease ignored by government and foreign powers alike, were statistics that did not disturb me. I was told that

that's how things had always been in China and always
would be.

I didn't get any help in these matters at school. The
Shanghai Public School for Girls was based strictly on an
English curriculum channelled toward the Cambridge University entrance examinations. Almost everything we
learned in history and geography related to Britain and the
British Empire. From time to time I heard about the bizarre
phenomenon of someone called Gandhi going on long periods of fasting to bend the arm of the Empire. Gandhi was
viewed with cynicism and some contempt among my elders.
He was a troublemaker. When I grew a foot in height at the
age of thirteen or so and became distressingly thin, I was
told I looked like Gandhi. He was a figure of fun. At school
we learned nothing of Chinese history or geography, or
social conditions or current government policies. We were
taught as if we lived on an island in the middle of an ocean,
an ocean whose ebb and flow had nothing to do with us. We
were taught French, but not even the rudiments of Chinese.
I could not read a word on any of the hundreds of banners
and shop-signs displayed in the streets. I never understood
anything of what the Chinese around me said. I grew up
with the curious impression that the Chinese were a no-
account people, with a no-account language and a history
that was of no account whatsoever. Only my father tried
from time to time to enlighten me but I was far too busy
committing my entire curriculum to my fly-paper memory
and playing tennis to pay any attention.

I did not worry. Like everyone else in the International
Settlement of Shanghai I put my trust in the might of Britain, in the inviolability of that Settlement and in Chiang
Kai-shek. No-one told me of the corruption at the heart of
the Chinese government, of the perfidy, the lack of concern
for human life. Perhaps they did not know themselves.

And so those guns at the end of August, 1937, were
shocking indeed. That first night we fell asleep to their

pounding, to the rattle of machine-gun fire and the penetrating crack of rifles. The next morning we woke to the same. We could smell the smoke wafting from the burning Chinese cities around the Settlement. There were phone calls all morning from worried relatives and friends. My doctor uncle and my Aunt Lena, and my cousin Nina, vacationing far away in Kuling, a two-day journey up the Yangtze River by boat, were the cause of much concern. The night before on our local radio station, RUOK, vacationing foreigners were advised to stay where they were, on no account to return to Shanghai, and the warning had been repeated that morning. The doctor was due back soon and the question was whether, in spite of this strongly-worded advice, he would return to his patients who awaited him so anxiously, or would he stay in the safety of Kuling?

In the middle of the morning my Aunt Lida, who had been left to look after the doctor's apartment, arrived at our house to discuss the emergency with my parents. They talked in frightened voices around the dining-room table where Ah Foh, our houseboy, served them with tea, his face drawn, his beaming, yellow-toothed smile for once not in evidence. The postal services and the telegraph lines had been disrupted. No-one could get in touch with our relatives. Following upon Aunt Lida, Uncle Ernest and Maria Mikhailovna dropped in to join the impromptu party and the conversation gathered momentum and voices heightened, while my father lighted cigarette after cigarette with shaky hands. It was very still and hot and the smoke drifted slowly out of the open French windows.

My mother now brought Ah Foh into the conference. What should be done about food supplies? Ah Foh reported that rice shops were locked and under guard for fear of looting by the thousands of refugees crowding into the city. Aunt Lida said she had seen the struggling lines of trudging people, their pitiful belongings, bedding and cooking utensils, laden on anything with wheels. At one point she and other pedestrians would have been unable to cross the street if it had not been for a stalwart Sikh policeman who had stopped the flow for a few moments. Uncle Ernest said that the Health Department predicted epidemics, they could never handle such an influx of people. There were no homes for these fugitives from terror, and no food. There could indeed be riots.

To the sound of the distant explosions we sat around the table drinking tea and nibbling biscuits and talking, and Ah Foh in a rather spotty apron, leaned against the door jamb and joined the discussion like another family member. But he did not sit down with us at the table and he was not offered any tea or biscuits though his future was as much at stake as ours, and though we would now have to depend upon him more than we had ever done, for he knew the tidal undertows of the city as we did not. If anyone would know where to find food and fuel at a true pinch, he would.

Uncle Ernest turned on the radio and we heard that the Settlement had closed its doors to any further refugees from the adjacent Chinese cities. The Shanghai Volunteer Corps had been posted at all points of ingress and they were turning back the flood. The Settlement was already filled to overflowing. Residents were advised to conserve their food and fuel. The rumour was that gas would be in short supply as the storage tanks had apparently been lowered for fear of direct hits. It was getting on for afternoon, so my mother suggested to our visitors that they stay for tiffin and I offered to go to the neighbourhood store to buy some sausage particularly favoured by Uncle Ernest who was something of a gourmet, and a few other groceries. My mother was doubtful about my going, but agreed after a short argument. After all we were miles away from the northeastern sector of the city, from the Whangpoo River, the Japanese Consulate and the "Idzuma."

I liked going to this particular store. It was Russian-owned and called Victory Store. There were shelves of cereals and canned and bottled food, and a delicatessen counter where cheeses, sausages, salads and cold meats were neatly arranged in succulent rows. My mother never bought delicatessen items from Chinese stores. It was a centre for neighbourhood chitchat, and glasses of beer and vodka, and orangeade and lemonade for the ladies, were served from behind the counter. At the entrance to the store there was a slot machine, and sometimes if I had an extra ten-cent piece in my pocket I would slip it in, pull the arm and watch for three strawberries or apples or lemons to show up. Nothing like that ever happened, but there was always hope, and I was once present at a magic moment when a neighbour hit the jackpot and in a sweep of expansiveness bought me an ice-cream bar.

Although all of these were interesting features, and I enjoyed the chatter and was delightedly shocked when one of the men would get tipsy and be dragged off home by an indignant wife, they were not the main attractions in the store for me. In the winter I went to Victory Store for the chocolate. Huge blocks of chocolate, one dark and bitter and one milk, sat on top of the counter by the till. These blocks were smartly cracked apart by the store owner with a wooden-headed hammer and the fragments of your choice were dropped into a wax paper bag and weighed. I was allowed to buy this chocolate on weekends and I always chose the milky variety. And in the summer I went to Victory Store for the ice-cream. At the beginning of May a wonderful freezer would arrive holding Hazelwood icecream bars. All though the summer I went to buy a bar every day after tiffin. It was with this in mind that I had made my offer to go and get the groceries. If I laid my bar straight on the ice in our ice-box it would keep till I had snatched a hasty tiffin.

But when I got to the store that day the people there were talking in frightened, excited voices. As the store owner weighed out the sausage for Uncle Ernest and packed it in a bag with the bread and other groceries on my list, I heard that something terrible had just happened downtown. Something unconscionable, but no-one knew exactly what it was. Rumours abounded. It seemed that bombs had fallen. It seemed that bombs had fallen on the *inviolable Settlement*!

Unprecedentedly, I skipped the Hazelwood bar and the slot-machine gamble and hurried home with my groceries, my mouth dry with dread. If the Japanese were bombing the Settlement, if the fighting was no longer confined to the northeastern sector and the river, then *no-one* was safe. *We* weren't safe. I came home and was greeted by horror-stricken relatives and the news on the radio. It was true. Bombs *had* been dropped on the Settlement, a number of bombs. Thousands of people had been killed.

No-one knew who had dropped the bombs. Crews were working in the stricken areas. During the day the busy streets downtown were usually filled wall to wall with people and traffic. And this crush was now augmented by the refugees. It was not difficult to imagine the carnage. The Transport Company of the Shanghai Volunteer Corps had been assigned to help in removing the dead and the wounded. The Transport Company. My main swain, not a day away from a lighthearted flirtatious tennis match under clear skies would be plunged into the task of sorting dead and wounded people, people torn apart by bombs. But I could not register any more horror. The thought drummed against a numbed brain.

Some time later a friend down the lane phoned and asked if she could borrow some valerian drops from us for her ageing mother who was close to collapse. This mother was known for her bouts of paranoia on the slightest pretext and this was indeed an opportunity for a good show. So distressed was she that our neighbour dared not leave her to go to the pharmacy. My mother, muttering about psychopaths, sent me across with a bottle of the drops with strict injunctions not to loiter. On my way back I saw a cluster of people at the entrance to the lane. In spite of my instructions to return immediately and to hug the shelter of the houses, I joined the cluster. They were watching trucks passing down the road. The trucks were laden with the gruesome remains of the bombing victims, haphazardly covered over with tarpaulins. I saw an arm hanging out at one end, a foot at the other. I hurried home. I said nothing to my mother. I wished I had listened to her and come straight home.

At home my mother was busy on the phone. Alarmed and alarmist friends formed a network, somewhat disquieting but in a sense also comforting. We were comforted to know that they cared, although in truth their alarm only augmented ours. The wife of the family dentist called in tears at the absence of my doctor uncle. She was an orphan of the Russian Revolution and a protégée of my Aunt Lena, and was in the habit of recounting all the woes of her married life to my aunt. The dentist was an eccentric who hated teeth and her life with him was disastrous, but she adored him. She wanted to commiserate with my mother on the unknown fate of our relations and to tell us she had heard dismaying rumours of foreigners being killed in the hinterland. "You know she's a fool," my Aunt Lida said angrily, but my mother was not comforted. A high nervous flush rose to her cheeks.

Dr. Gerber, once a general practitioner, now an opthalmologist and an ear, nose and throat specialist, rang to assure us that he would be standing by while my doctor uncle was away. We should not hesitate to call him should need arise.

"He's so upset he couldn't remember my name," my mother cried. "What help would he be?" But that was unfair which she readily admitted, for although we all giggled as a release from our own tension, we knew that the droll little doctor, frenziedly meticulous in his work, had indeed come to our aid in times past.

Mrs. Rezzini, the wife of a wealthy Russianized Italian

28

importer, phoned to tell us that her husband had access to food supplies and would help us out if need arose. We should be out buying right now, she advised. Prices could only go up. Had we heard anything from the doctor, she wanted to know.

There was a knock on the door and I opened it to admit a neighbour who handed me a currant cake still warm from the oven. She had been baking when the news of the bombing came on the radio. She wanted to share her cake before we were all blown to bits. As we were cutting into the cake the phone rang yet again. It was Nyuta Mayeseyevna, Nina's piano teacher, worrying about her family of cats. What would she do with them if there was to be no food?

"She can always eat them," my Uncle Ernest snorted, and earned a sharp rebuke from his wife, while I repressed yet another nervous giggle and stuffed my mouth full of currant cake.

"The less you talk on that phone the better," my father said, feverishly lighting another cigarette.

Day after day the fighting continued. Now even the residential streets, far from the points of ingress from the Chinese cities, well removed from the areas where the main body of the refugees had congregated, were transformed by the migration. The city took on the look of a shanty town. The refugees spread everywhere, setting up camp under mats stretched over bamboo poles and under oilpaper umbrellas. They slept on the ground, the luckier ones on mattresses or quilts, the luckless ones straight on the cement. Soon they were starving. The Chinese had sunk ships across the Yangtze to prevent the Japanese from moving up-river to Nanking, and the blockade also prevented supplies from the hinterland from reaching Shanghai. Other routes had to be found. In the meantime the Settlement faced a food crisis.

Taking Mrs. Rezzini's advice Mother and Ah Foh had wasted no time and had gone shopping to places he recommended bringing home rice and flour and beans in large sacks, loaded on a rickshaw. She had also stocked up with cheese, dry salami and canned goods, jam, peanut butter and coffee. Meat and vegetables would not keep, there would doubtless be a shortage of ice for our icebox. Gas was in very short supply for the tanks had indeed been lowered. We would have to lay in a supply of coal because we might have to cook on Ah Foh's outdoor chattie. My mother made plans to go downtown to order the coal, as she had always done this chore. Orders for coal had to be placed in person and paid for in cash. Her plans were angrily vetoed by my father. His office had been shut down as it was too close to the main combat arena. Unwillingly, he was having the first holiday of his life. He did not want to go downtown and he did not want Mother to go either. The closure of his office meant that we would be short of money. Tempers were frayed. It was the closest I had ever heard my parents come to a quarrel.

The British and the Americans began to evacuate their women and children from the Settlement to Hong Kong. It was desirable, they said, that women and children, and even men not engaged in the protection of the Settlement, should leave in order to conserve food and fuel for the defending forces. Some of my British girlfriends had already left. Once in a while I heard from the swains, and my main swain came to visit briefly, between duty shifts, in his Shanghai Volunteer Corps uniform smelling of dust and khaki. His visit did not please me—I had always managed to meet my summer friends away from my embarrassing home—but he did not care about my house nor who my parents were. He had seen dead people, people blown to bits. He had helped to clean up the bits. He looked tired and haggard. He never stayed long. We sat on chairs awkwardly separated from each other. There was a different feeling in our relationship. The lightheartedness was gone. He was more intense and I somehow curiously removed. My relationship with him did not fit into the present situation. It had been a midsummer fantasy and it had been the group that had made the fantasy so dynamic. Alone, he could not maintain the illusion.

One day my sister's husband phoned in some distress. A mortar bomb had exploded outside their apartment window and my sister had suffered shellshock. My brother-in-law wanted to evacuate her and he thought I should go too. I would be safe in Hong Kong. I wasn't British, which might be a stumbling block, but if I were willing to go, and if my parents agreed, he would try to pull some strings.

I didn't want to go and neither did my shaken sister, but my brother-in-law was adamant and my parents pressed me to go along with his wishes. As the people pushing the evacuation said, it would be the sensible course to take. There were bound to be severe food shortages and there was always danger from the continuing Japanese offensive. Missiles intended for the Chinese cities were falling on Yangtzepoo and Hongkew, the east end of my childhood, as well as other outlying parts of the Settlement. It had now been established that the bombs that had fallen on the inner Settlement had been dropped accidentally. More accidents like that could well happen. Stray shells were a constant threat like the one that had blown up outside my sister's apartment. There was no problem about money. My brother-in-law had the necessary funds for our passages and our living expenses. If I went I would provide company and comfort for my sister who was far from well. She would appreciate a companion. Put that way I did not need any more persuasion. Of course I would go if my sister needed me.

So it was settled. We were to go to Hong Kong.

Chapter Three

My world was collapsing around me like the city of card houses my sister had built for me once so long ago, the card city that had collapsed from a real tremor of the earth, but I was too frightened and too confused to assess the true significance of the present turn of events. I did not realize that what I was witnessing was the imminent end of an era, an era the likes of which would never be seen again, a style of life that was soon to disappear forever, its manifestation and its passing as strange and as sad as the blossoming and swift death of a rare exotic bloom.

I had been living in a dream, a dream of childhood in which events and emotions were contained within concentric rings of watchful adults, first a family ring, and beyond that a ring of family friends. Both family and friends had been steeped in unreality, presences that had their nebulous being around me but of whose inner workings I was as innocent as I was of the functionings of the cosmos.

My dream had been of an alien city full of wonders, where the people who truly belonged there, as I did not, spoke a language I did not understand but which filled the air with the mystery of its incantation and spoke of realms beyond my understanding. In this city promised delights were assured and threats held at bay by those same rings of adults, all powerful and all kind, adults who had come to live in this alien city for reasons vague to me but somehow urgently imperative to them. And that I was the treasured centre of this roundabout, to be served and preserved forever, I had no doubt.

When I was about twelve an anxiety attack suffered by my mother had triggered a change in me. I had suddenly seen my parents as people apart from myself. I had become aware of their mortality. I had even—once—harboured a tremulous suspicion, quickly banished, that I was not the epicentre of their world. But apart from these glimpses into reality I had not made many more inroads into their lives as persons. To a great extent I still accepted them simply as reservoirs of comfort and convenience to me.

The dream of childhood broadened, its stage became more accommodating. Adventure beckoned from the wings, and longings for distant climes, for love, romance. In my city spring triumphed early over sharp, short winters, magnolias blossomed at the first breath of March and the song of cicadas filled blue, sun-soaked days. I spent my summer-afternoon siestas reading and dozing to the cries of itinerant pedlars, gentle and melodic, riding the steaming stillness, and every night I fell asleep to the ancient, comforting voices of the frogs serenading the splendour of the enigmatic eastern moons. But the stage I was setting for myself was still contained within the same circles of protective adults, I was still as separated from the outer world as a chick is by its shell.

The sound of those guns on that August evening cracked the magic shell. The events of Bloody Saturday as it was immediately dubbed, catapulted me out of those charmed circles into the actual world. I discovered my parents, my aunts and uncles, my sister, the neighbour with the paranoid mother, the wife of the dentist who hated teeth, the music teacher with her cat family, as vessels full of a living essence in whose depths I now saw reflected my own alarm and horror. They sprang to life before my wakened eyes, no longer vague apparitions hedging my dreams, but as threatened and concerned persons suddenly moving in on my insularity, suddenly challenging centre stage. Their fears were as real as mine!

And now I was to leave them. A date was set, passages booked. Once again I packed a suitcase although with vastly different feelings from those I had experienced only a short year ago when I had packed for my holiday in the north. The evening before our departure my main swain came to say

33

goodbye. He was in his uniform, collar loosened, damp with perspiration. He was upset at my leaving. He made me promise to write to him and kissed me chastely before he went. I felt some warmth and a sadness, as in the parting from a good friend, and also a little guilt that our separation did not seem as dispiriting to me as it did to him, but I didn't feel much else. Somehow the spark had gone out for me, although perhaps not for him. In me it had been doused by fear and confusion.

We were to assemble the following morning in a hotel downtown close to the Bund. From this hotel we were to be bused to a British gunboat that would then ferry us along the Whangpoo River to the S.S. Shenking lying at anchor at the mouth of the Yangtze, beyond the reach of the guns. The S.S. Shenking would take us to Hong Kong.

So the next morning sees my sister and me getting into a cab and after somewhat tearful farewells we are driven to the hotel downtown.

As we drive through the crowded streets, in spite of the knowledge that by leaving the city we are helping to conserve food and fuel for those remaining, I can't help feeling badly. All the wealthy women and children are able to get away and the people without influence or money or a powerful consulate behind them, people like my parents, my relatives, like our emigrant friends, have to stay behind to face the dangers of the war simply because they can't afford to go. The differences between privileged members of the community and the disadvantaged have always been a galling factor in my life but the unfairness has never before been so blatantly apparent. Even though this time I am somehow on the other side of the fence, the sense of wrong sits on my heart like a lump of wet clay.

I am also very frightened as we drive toward the centre of town and my fear deepens when we arrive at the hotel, the place of assembly. The corner where the first bomb fell only a week ago is just a few blocks away. Planes zoom overhead

34

constantly, gunfire is continuous, distressingly close and loud. There is no protection for us should another bomb fall. I have never felt such bone-deep terror as I experience now sitting silently on a suitcase in the lobby. In a state bordering on liquefaction I wait for the buses to arrive or for a bomb to fall.

The buses make it first. I have to hold myself back from pushing to get on board, force myself to remain quietly in line, just hoping there will be room for us on the first bus so that the clutch of controlled hysteria can be loosened from my chest. There isn't room for us on the first bus, but we board the second, and time stands still while the bus crawls out of the hotel driveway into the road and then chugs at a pace that seems purposely slow down to the wharves, toward the now even more pronounced barrage of fire.

At the wharf we all but fall into the helpful arms of the friendly British tars on board one of the gunboats. They take us below where it's safest and we start on the trip down the Whangpoo River to the mouth of the Yangtze. The sailors serve us hot tea with milk and sugar and joke and flirt mildly, and we are wooed out of our state of stiff-necked panic, even though the whole trip is being made to the whistling of shells overhead, their crashing on the other side of the river, and the eerie echoes from shore to shore. The Chinese forces are solidly entrenched and the Japanese task is turning out to be more difficult than they thought.

We have to climb aboard the S.S. Shenking by way of a swaying rope-ladder lowered to the deck of the gunboat. The sailors steady the ladder and laugh at our nervousness, and we are all soon safely stowed on board the ship. The S.S. Shenking is a middle-sized coastal steamer ploughing the seas along the China coast and probably picking up quite a packet from the purses of the panic-stricken residents of Shanghai. That night, as the ship moves out onto the rolling sea and we leave the war behind us, I have a great dinner to celebrate my release from terror, but my stomach is tied in such knots that I am horribly sick in the cabin. I relieve myself of my dinner in the sink, which is promptly plugged up and we have to call in the ship's handyman to my poor sister's enormous embarrassment.

The Evacuation Committee has assigned us to billets and my sister and I find ourselves in a boarding-house on a street called Mody Road. It's in Kowloon, part of the mainland facing the island of Hong Kong across a stretch of boat-studded water and communicating with Hong Kong by the Star Ferries.

When we arrive at the boarding-house we find that we have a large room on the main floor. What surprises us is that two other women, though they arrived earlier, have been placed in a rather narrow enclosed verandah separated from our room by French windows. We can't imagine why we have been thus favoured. We soon discover our mistake, we're not advantaged at all, for while their verandah has been made totally private, with the help of some drapes rigged up over the French windows, our room is a passage-way for them in and out of the verandah. They walk by us often during the day, smiling their apologies, and at night I can hear them creeping in and out of our room, past our large double bed on their way to the bathroom located off the hall. My sister puts all our valuables under her pillow, not for fear of being burgled by the verandah ladies, but because we can never be sure whether they have remembered to lock our door after their midnight sorties.

Our sojourn in Hong Kong does not start off auspiciously for me. One night soon after our arrival, I waken from a nightmare and find that I have to make a trip to the bath-room. Usually I am a sound sleeper and seldom need to visit at night, and even when I'm disturbed by the passing through of the verandah ladies I'm able to drop off quite quickly. But this night is different. I creep out, hoping to wake no-one and intending to make it to the bathroom without putting on the hall light. I know that if I guide myself by the hall table where we find our mail in the mornings I can make it to the door of the bathroom without any trouble.

As I move out into the hall, I am arrested by a very strange sound, a kind of low sizzling. I imagine it might be something to do with the waterworks in the bathroom. In the dense darkness I put out my hand and lay my palm firmly on the trusty hall table, but to my fright the tabletop slithers away from under my hand and the sizzling rises to a crescendo of frenzied rustling. I let out a bellow that brings my sister, the verandah ladies and several lodgers from upstairs bounding out of their beds. The hall light is switched on and I see that the entire hall table, and indeed much of the floor, is covered with huge, four-inch-long flying cockroaches.

I am not unacquainted with flying cockroaches and although they are claimed to be harmless they fill me with brain-numbing horror. We have them in Shanghai all through the summer and they often fly in to shelter behind the picture mouldings, from which hiding-place we can see their huge feelers waving defiantly, but I have never seen quite such large ones, and never a whole colony at once. The landlady assures us that they must have come in through the open hall window, that it's some kind of migration and nothing to do with her housekeeping, and the verandah ladies say *they've* never seen them before, making me feel as if I myself have conjured up the monsters by some nefarious witchcraft. The landlady says she will shut the lights and open the front door and they'll leave. We all go back to our beds but no amount of reassurance can ameliorate my trauma and nothing short of fire will ever persuade me to traverse that hall again after lights out. The cockroaches are denizens of the night and we make a special effort to tuck in our mosquito nets securely before settling down to sleep.

Downtown Hong Kong in 1937 is not very different from Shanghai. The streets are as crowded and as filthy, as hot and

37

dusty. I find a shorthand-and-typing school run by a cheerful and kind Chinese gentleman called Mr. Law. It's situated in an ancient brick building and the classroom is large and high-ceilinged if somewhat dingy. We learn to type on stiff-keyed Underwood typewriters. Mr. Law is an excellent instructor and we all progress famously. He's the first Chinese I come to regard as a real person. With my flypaper brain, shorthand is a cinch. We bring our lunch in paper bags and eat on a wide verandah that runs the length of the old building and has collected the dust and leaves of years in its corners and crevices. Every day, when we have finished eating our lunch, a young Chinese boy brings around little paper cups of ice cream, courtesy of Mr. Law. There's a dairy quite close to the school. It's an affectionate touch and excellent psychology.

I travel back and forth to Mr. Law's school on the Star Ferry with other students who live in Kowloon. The trips are full of fun and sun and water sparkle. I become the recipient of many confidences, the kind that young people are so eager to make and receive, but though I learn many fascinating secrets on the Star Ferry, I reveal little of myself. I have long ago learned to hold my tongue while lending a ready ear to the outpourings of others. I give factual information when I'm asked—the war? scary; my sister? the best; Shanghai? pretty *big*. And what's snow like, asks a girl from Canton who's saving her money to go north in the winter with the sole purpose of seeing snow. But I never divulge any deep emotions. I never tell anyone about my home, or my emigrant status. I let them draw their own conclusions as to how I am associated with a British evacuation. I don't mention my successes at school and I never speak of boyfriends nor of the bleak feelings of nostalgia that sweep over me when I think back to the idyllic summer only a few weeks behind me.

Hong Kong is a duty-free port and my sister takes full advantage of this. We visit the East-Indian dress-goods shops on Nathan Road and pore over colours and styles. I need a new coat for the winter and we decide on a rich dark-green wool. This beautiful material will be transformed with uncanny skill by my mother and my Aunt Lida into the desired garment. My sister chooses elegant dress silks for gifts for the folks back home, and she buys, and I joyfully consume, unrestricted quantities of duty-free chocolate that give me the worst case of acne in teenage history. I'm glad none of my swains are there to see me, and I lay off the chocolate. As a special treat we sometimes go out to have tea at a lovely little teashop that serves the most delicious cakes. It's foreign-owned and we're sure it's beyond suspicion in regard to cleanliness.

My sister's firm has moved to Hong Kong and she goes back to work for them. She seems to have recovered from her shellshock. She tries to be cheerful and succeeds well enough, but I know she's missing her husband by her eager sorting of the mail and her worry shows when she scans the paper for news of the Shanghai hostilities.

I do not suffer in that way. A curious facet of my personality surfaces for the first time during these months of exile. It appears that I develop a kind of stolidity in the face of adversity. I manage to block out the anxiety that hovers on the skirts of my awareness and I live in the present, withdrawing to a secret place within myself. Here I sometimes compose poetry, which I never show to anyone. It's an enchanted place, at once strange and familiar and I keep it to myself, much in the way I used to keep the tiny porcelain dog my sister gave me when I was little, secret and deep in my pocket.

Functioning out of my private hideaway, I am able to adapt swiftly to new conditions. I'm becoming very much involved with my life in Hong Kong and I'm settling well into my surroundings. I give my whole attention to my studies and my new skills delight me. I find that I'm almost beginning to resent the letters that keep coming in from my family and my main swain reminding me that I have other, prior loyalties. I correspond dutifully with my family and I do my best to write affectionately to my swain, but as the days go by my sense of detachment and indifference makes this writing more and more difficult. I wonder about this, but there is something in Hong Kong that is very attractive to me though I don't know what it is.

Our life is not without its problems. A cholera epidemic closes off all the beaches and we drink only hot tea, for though we have had our cholera shots and though we know that all those people dying are poor and uninoculated Chinese, we still wonder exactly how safe we are. Our favourite restaurant where we have been having those delicious teas and in whose cleanliness we put our utmost trust, is closed down. A waiter turns out to be a typhoid carrier. And we live through the Great Typhoon.

One night we wake up to the sound of an unusual wind, and the verandah ladies rattling around, struggling to shut their windows. A typhoon has been predicted but we have not paid much attention to the warnings. We're used to typhoons. In Shanghai the most damage they ever do is knock down a few billboards, and uproot some trees. True, sometimes the city is flooded, sewage surfaces from pipes that can never be laid deep enough in the swampy ground, and an unholy mess ensues. But we're ferried across impassable streets by rickshaw coolies who are only too glad to get the extra fares. No-one worries if these coolies become ill or die from wading in the filth because rickshaw coolies die all the time anyway. We only grumble at how much they charge. And everything's over in a couple of days. So typhoons do not frighten us, and in fact in Shanghai we welcome them because they give us a break from the intolerable heat. During the summer I've often seen my father up on our roof garden, covered with prickly-heat rash, gazing in longing out to the horizon where a few cauliflower-shaped clouds are clustered, praying that they might be the forerunners of a storm.

But we soon find out that typhoons in Hong Kong are quite different. By the time typhoons reach Shanghai they've lost most of their power, but they strike Hong Kong with their full force. All night long the wind rages and roars, old Mody House shakes and groans under its repeated assaults and the verandah ladies pray. The howling of the wind is eerie after the unbroken chain of long, hot, still nights. We sleep fitfully and I wonder how the cockroaches are doing.

In the morning we're exhausted. The strength of the wind has abated, but we hear reports of damage, lives lost. People on the swanky Peak have had all their windows blown in and have been obliged to spend the night in cold, rain-sodden houses. Plate-glass windows in the famous Peninsula Hotel have also suffered. Small craft have been badly battered and people have died but since these were Chinese lives no count is made and they hardly rate at all compared to the broken windows in the homes of the rich. But the sensation of the storm is the beaching of the giant liner, the S.S. Conte Verde. When the storm abates we go to see the grounded monster. It's impressive. The ship lies on her side, high and dry. She looks naked and helpless. There are hundreds of people gawking at her humiliation. My sister says it's a lesson to man. Man is too smug about his achievements, she says, nature still holds the upper hand.

I have an adventure. My friends persuade me to go on a picnic to a beach many miles away. We travel by bus and since we have been cautioned against the contaminated beaches we walk a long way to a clean flowing stream where we have our picnic. We have bread and cold canned baked beans, a treat. Crossing the stream over slippery stones I fall and injure my foot. The pain is excruciating. I can't walk back to the highway so two of the boys cross their arms and carry me, but it is slow going. When we reach the bus stop we see the back of a disappearing bus. We sink down on the banked side of the road and resign ourselves to a half-hour wait. When a bus does come along it's full and doesn't stop. Neither does the second nor the third. It's now late and very dark on the deserted highway. One of the boys says that bandits have been reported on this stretch of road who rob people of their money and jewellery and if their rings don't come off easily they chop off their fingers, and their heads if their necklaces get stuck. One of the girls starts to cry and the boy says he was just kidding, but I know he wasn't because the verandah ladies told us about just such a case.

Suddenly we see a dark shape heading our way and we all tighten with apprehension, but a faint beam of wavering light reassures us—it's a Chinese policeman on a bicycle. He is heading for home, but when we explain our plight he promises to get us on the next bus. He rests his cycle against the bank and settles down to wait. When the headlights of yet another bus appear he leaps into the centre of the road brandishing his truncheon and yelling. We gasp, expecting to see him run down, but are instead amazed and gratified to see the bus stop. It is also full but the policeman speaks peremptorily to the conductor who shouts at the people on the bus to make room and we squeeze in. We thank the policeman profusely, and he salutes, grinning broadly, pleased to show off his authority. He would have lost a lot of face if the driver had ignored him.

My sister has been worried half to death, she soaks my foot in cold water and helps me to bed. I sleep and dream of bandits on dark deserted roads sorting out rings and fingers.

One morning we have a surprise cable. Nina and my doctor uncle and my Aunt Lena are arriving by boat from Canton and have booked into the Peninsula Hotel. They would like us to meet them at the hotel that very afternoon!

We wonder what they can possibly be doing in Canton. When we left Shanghai there was still no news of them from their Kuling summer hideaway and we all presumed they had decided to wait out the war in the safety of the resort.

Kuling is hundreds of miles from Canton, far to the north-west.

We're intrigued and excited at the thought of seeing them again, and we're at the hotel before they arrive. They are tanned from their vacation and exhausted by their trip. The doctor is anxious to get back to Shanghai and to his patients, his vacation is long over, but the Yangtze River has been blockaded, no ships are going through, so they have had to make a long detour by train to Canton and Hong Kong. From Hong Kong they will take the first available boat back to Shanghai. The doctor wants to leave Aunt Lena and Nina in Hong Kong, but they won't hear of it. They're all going back together. The doctor will need their help in the beleaguered city, they say.

When I realize that my Aunt Lena and Nina are actually going to go back, under gunfire and exposed to possible bombing, to the city which other prestigious wealthy nationals have left to its fate, my attitude toward my emigrant relatives undergoes a radical change. I have always been aware of the integrity of that little family and of their loyalty to one another, but this move signifies more than that. It signifies their devotion to duty and to the welfare of the people who have been left behind in that city, helpless in the face of ugly odds. A staunchness runs through all three of them, a resilience in the face of adversity, a capacity to dismiss danger when duty is in question. I feel proud of them, almost envious of the role they are adopting, and overwhelmed with shame at ever having felt any embarrassment in regard to my emigrant relatives because of their shaky English and because they belong to what seems to me to be an outlandish and archaic church. It's a major change in my thinking, a dramatic moment of awareness.

Their visit with us is brief, but it's a welcome interlude. We feel like old residents of Hong Kong and give them guided tours. We visit the Peak on the tramway that makes all the water reservoirs look as if they're standing on end, and we ride up and down on the automatic elevator in the Hong Kong and Shanghai Bank building, the only true sky-scraper in Hong Kong at that time and the first boasting an elevator with no attendant. It's scary to press a button and then trust to the machinery without anyone to depend on in case of disaster. We drive out to Repulse Bay on one of the double-decker buses, the narrow winding road making it a hair-raising trip. My Aunt Lena treats us to dinners at the Peninsula Hotel and I wish I hadn't eaten so much duty-free chocolate as I am very conscious of my spotty face in the midst of such grand surroundings.

At last they leave on a very creaky ship called the S.S. Andre le Bon. We wave goodbye from the pier and feel sad and deserted.

As the days pass I become more and more attached to Kowloon, to Hong Kong, to the vistas of great seas, to the Star Ferry, to the verandah ladies, to Mr. Law and his stiff typewriters and his ice-cream treats, to the girl who's saving her money for a trip to see snow. I become attached to my new friends and to Nathan Road and the gutteral-voiced Indians who sell beautiful silks and to Mody Road and the ramshackle Mody House with its cockroaches. So it's with a jolt almost of regret that I see a huge poster one day as I step out of Mr. Law's business school that says CEASEFIRE IN SHANGHAI. Newspaper boys are running around shout-ing, and people on the streets and on the pier, obviously Shanghai evacuees, are cavorting with joy, and I know that I too should be joyful, and perhaps even cavort. But I don't cavort, and I can't understand why I'm not more joyful.

I go home to Mody House and there's my sister being joy-ful too, though she isn't the type to cavort, and the verandah ladies also are joyful and almost cavorting for they both run out to hug me and spin me around, but I feel depressed. There will be another leave-taking.

We put our names down for return trips to Shanghai and are told that we can board the S.S. Conte Biancamano in a few days. We get an extra suitcase for our assortment of purchases, and my sister starts packing right away, but the sadness haunts me. My family, my friends, the swains, Victory Terrace, the church, have all assumed an unreality I'm loath to disturb. It isn't that I'm not mightily relieved in the knowledge that the killing has ended, of course I am, but I can't rouse myself to any great enthusiasm for the return trip.

We make the trip on the luxurious S.S. Conte Biancamano, sister ship to the battered S.S. Conte Verde, and very soon we sail into the muddy waters of the Whangpoo River and see the familiar skyline of the Bund, and in no time we are looking down on the wharves of Shanghai, full of carts and chanting coolies and the whining of hoists and crashing and shouting, and there on the jetty to meet us are Nina and my Uncle Ernest, my sister's husband and my main swain. My father is at work and my mother busy preparing a dinner for us.

We all talk at once, and laugh and carry on, but I feel an emptiness beneath it all and an overlay of guilt at my lack of true enthusiasm. Someone says that there's always a letdown when adversity comes to an end and its challenges cease to motivate its victims, and maybe that's it, but somehow I know there is more. It is as if I have left something behind in Hong Kong, something more significant than the everyday routines of my temporary exile, more compelling than the charm of its easy-going ways, deeper than the friendships I made. I do not know what it is, but it badgers me, and I think about it a good deal.

45

Chapter Four

And one day, about a month later, I recognize what it is that I left behind in Hong Kong. The realization comes to me in a circuitous manner, possibly the way of all realizations, and it comes during a particularly festive evening at my Aunt Lena's home.

19 December was always a great day in our family. It was St. Nicholas' day in the calendar of the Russian Orthodox Church and therefore the name's-day of my doctor uncle, Nicholas Kusnetzov. It was the Russian custom for well-wishers to drop in on all name's-day celebrants without invitation and it was a custom much-respected and greatly in vogue. Both Aunt Lena and Nina observed their name's-days too, but no name's-day was as noteworthy as my doctor uncle's. Because he was such a well-known and loved figure in the Russian emigrant community, few failed to put in an appearance to offer their felicitations and to have a cup of tea or a glass of wine and sample some of the delectable "zakuski" off the buffet table or a slice or two of the toothsome cakes and tortes spread out on white linen among cascades of flowers.

All morning long the doorbell rang in my aunt's house and offerings of flowers and fruit, chocolates and other gifts came pouring in. The visiting started in the early afternoon and continued late into the evening. As my uncle grew in popularity my Aunt Lena found it necessary to hire caterers and extra help as she could no longer cope with the influx by herself.

A week before the affair Mother and I made a traditional trip to a curious place of business in a dingy lane off the famous Avenue Joffre, the main artery of the French Concession. This was the office of a confectioner who specialized in one certain kind of torte. It was called a mikada, and comprised wafers and chocolate fill, and the crispness of its tex-

46

ture and the richness of its chocolate still make me feel faint from ecstasy at the mere memory. The confectioner who had his office in the dingy lane was famous throughout the city for his mikada tortes, and every year it was our gift to my doctor uncle. My mother placed the order and money changed hands and we left feeling proud that we had actually ordered a mikada. I never saw the cakes being made, but sure as sunrise, year after year, our order was delivered before noon on 19 December to my aunt's apartment.

My aunt's apartment was very large, for in addition to their own living space, it also contained the doctor's office and the waiting-room. On this day the waiting-room, which was out of bounds when we came to visit on other occasions and so had an air of some mystery about it, was recruited for the overflow of guests, and I loved to examine the pictures on the walls and the objets-d'art, especially a marble replica of the Venus de Milo, presented by Mr. Rezzini of fine foods fame, and discreetly draped by one of my aunt's scarves.

If my doctor uncle's name's-days were traditionally festive, the one falling on 19 December, 1937 was especially so.

The Japanese hostilities had ended and we had all survived. It was a cause for rejoicing. I recognized this even though a haze of depression still hovered over my mind. When I returned from Hong Kong it was like coming to a new city, a new life, so swiftly and absolutely had I adapted to the circumstances of my evacuation. I felt like a stranger. I missed Mr. Law's school and my Hong Kong friends. We had hugged and promised to write, but I knew within myself that I would probably never see them again, that they would forget me and I them. This knowledge, this new sorrow, matured me and deepened my awareness, and coming back to Shanghai as a kind of alien from another shore I began to notice things I had not noticed previously. I saw aspects of our life in that city of ruins and degradation that I had missed altogether prior to my short exile.

If, at the age of twelve, I had first become aware of my parents as persons removed from myself and subject to the law of mortality, I now began to see them even more clearly as entirely separate entities with their own lives to lead, their own hardships to overcome, their own emotions to handle. Recalling the quiet courage of my doctor uncle, Aunt Lena and Nina when they took it upon themselves to return to a city racked by war, I was able to look more closely, and with far more respect, at my other emigrant relatives and the emigrant friends and acquaintances whom I had eschewed during my mad sweet summer of the swains. I saw these persons as the stalwart folk they were, uprooted since the Russian revolution, drifting, battling displacement, sometimes failing but more often succeeding in somehow pulling their lives together, the people who had been forced to stay behind to face the problems of a city under fire when wealthy nationals had left, and had faced those problems with courage and resolution. When my father had jaundice, my mother and my Aunt Lida, in spite of my father's protests, had nonetheless ventured downtown close to the heart of the battle zone, to order the coal necessary to cook on Ah Foh's outdoor chattie.

"What could I do?" my mother said, "he needed chicken soup." They had waited out an air-raid in a damaged doorway. "How often does a bomb fall in the same place twice?" she had reasoned.

In the light of my own recent buffeting by a barrage of emotions I felt a new compassion, an admiration.

But there was also something else, another realization, and one that broke upon my mind that evening in a singular irradiation, like the light in certain paintings, not quite real but strikingly revealing, a moment I have never forgotten and that marked for me the start of a new struggle toward a goal that was as yet far distant and by no means defined in my own heart.

So on this 19 December, 1937, in mid-afternoon, my mother and I start out for my aunt's apartment. My father will follow later, toward dinner-time, he has never been fond of large gatherings and at this particular time he is still feeling the after effects of the jaundice from which he suffered during the Japanese hostilities. But my mother loves parties and she wouldn't want to miss a moment of this one. We take the bus instead of walking as it is cold and we are dressed in our best finery. My mother has a new hat that she has pinned securely to her hair. We ring the bell at my aunt's apartment and are let in by an unfamiliar houseboy who has just been hired as extra help. This novice beams and bows, takes my mother's coat and plucks the new hat off her head for good measure to her great chagrin and the amusement of nearby guests, for the hat drags her carefully arranged hair with it. I quash my instant desire to giggle—I know she has spent a long time in front of her mirror getting it just right.

My aunt's apartment is redolent of flowers and cigarette smoke, and a variety of perfumes, and the astringent odour of many humans gathered in a close space. My doctor uncle, in an immaculate suit, stands in the doorway between the hall and the dining-room, his hair and dark moustache meticulously trimmed, his hands folded, smiling quietly. He inclines his head to the guests as they arrive and they enter the dining-room to be greeted by my aunt whose attire, as always, is tasteful, and who looks dignified drawn up to her full height of 5′1″ (with heels). I eagerly survey the dining-room table, heaped with pastries and tortes to make sure that all my favourites are there. Our mikada stands proudly at one end but a piece has been cut out of it, someone has been at it already.

The doorbell rings and the door is opened to a gale of high-pitched laughter. I recognize the voice of the dentist's wife and turn around to greet both her and her husband. She is a large-boned, pretty woman whose gay public demeanour betrays none of the miseries of her life. An orphan of the revolution, she met her husband when he visited the orphanage to check on the teeth of the inmates. "When I looked up at him and saw those black eyes," she said to me once, "my heart died in my chest. It was the end." And it was the end for her. The dentist never fulfilled the expectations everyone had had of him as a young man truly skilled in his profession. Tanya had a few good years, but lately things have been going from bad to worse.

The dentist was a radio fanatic. He claimed the invention of the radio before Marconi. Every penny he made went into new and expensive equipment for his hobby. He was furious at the indifference of his friends, at the lack of acknowledgement from the world. *He had invented the radio,* and no-one cared. Some crazy Italian had got the credit. When I was little my mother and I often found him hunched over his shortwave set, his patients waiting. I remember hearing that he was losing clients. As time passed I began to hear that the dentist had given up the radio but had decided to breed tropical fish. There was money in rare fish, he said. He had spent more than he could afford on enormous aquariums and many exotic specimens.

They moved into a smaller apartment and on my visits I had been entranced by a strange underwater world. The apartment was humid and airless, the windows covered with blinds. It was densely hot in summer. There was even an aquarium in his actual office so that when you sat in his chair enduring drilling without anaesthetic, you could distract yourself from your pain by rolling your eyes around and observing various striped marvels swishing sleek bodies and tails in their electrically-lit habitat. More clients were lost.

I had been hearing lately that the fish experiment had failed, that the exotic fish were dying, that he was blaming merchants who, he claimed, had sold him inferior fish. We knew that Tanya had had to go out to work, that she helped out in the homes of the rich, sang in a choir and at parties, and that now the dentist was thinking of going into bee-keeping. There was money in honey. "He hates teeth," Tanya once said to my mother.

But now these heartbreaks are not apparent. The dentist has come in a tuxedo dating back to his wedding, complete with stiff white shirt and black bow-tie. He looks very dapper. Those who are not his clients would never guess at the shabbiness of his apartment; the loans my Aunt Lena has given to Tanya are kept secret. His small moustache is carefully manicured and the black eyes that made Tanya swoon are shining.

I move into the room with the cakes and meet Nyuta, Nina's piano teacher. Nina herself, stylishly dressed and charmingly flushed stands at the end of the room by the laden table, fending off compliments from a rakish admirer. Nyuta is balancing a cup of tea and nibbling at a pastry. I ask her how her cat family did during the Japanese hostilities. "Kind people helped me out," she replies. I know who those kind people were. My aunt always worries about Nyuta. Once she was white and pink and gold, pretty though scatter-brained, often late for the lessons she gave Nina, a compulsive talker and a fanatic about cleanliness. But a little while ago Nyuta lost her older sister, Tonya. Tonya had died of rabies. She had ignored a nip from a strange dog. There were whispered tales of the agonies of her death, how she had barked like a dog, howled.

A change had come over Nyuta. She had lost her fear of germs and had started to collect cats. She neglected her home and her person. Her teaching had become more and more slapdash. My aunt continued to pay for lessons that Nina had started to hate but she couldn't bear to hurt Nyuta's feelings.

I look at Nyuta closely. Her nose is heavily powdered in an effort to maintain an illusion of youth, but I can see the ravages of the trauma she has suffered. Her blouse is crumpled and not overclean, her hair is untidy, she eats greedily. A faint odour of cat wafts from her person. A vision of the Nyuta of my childhood flashes across my mind, Nyuta in her wide-brimmed lace-trimmed hats, white dresses, pink ribbons, tripping through the dusty, sunny streets of Shanghai, sporting a parasol, avoiding the dirt. Her fear of infections had been justified, but somehow in this cataclysmic justification the fear has vanished. It's all too confusing and I decide to have a slice of the mikada.

Cutting his way into the cake is Dr. Gerber. Dr. Gerber is the ophthalmologist and ear, nose and throat specialist who phoned my mother with offers of aid when the Japanese hostilities had broken out, and had forgotten her name at the critical moment. He has a domed skull with thin hair combed carefully across it. I get an unbearable seizure of the giggles and can scarcely return his polite greeting. Dr. Gerber receives his patients in the dining-room of a terrace house kept immaculate by his stout and unflappable wife. The table is pushed aside and an interesting mechanically-controlled chair has been installed. There is the usual sheet of test letters on the far wall and the little man hops from side to side of the chair peering into eyes and ears, noses and throats with an assortment of mysterious instruments. In my early years I was subject to earwax and for this he would call for a bowl of warm water, opening the dining-room door and projecting his request in a shaky voice into the dim recesses of a long corridor. The bowl would be delivered by his sister who suffered from nerve damage to one side of her face, the result of a tragic dental mishap dating to Tsarist days. Her face is sadly twisted and has always filled my heart with a rending pity and a lifelong terror of dentists.

When the cleansing of the ear was completed, Dr. Gerber would carefully examine the water in the dish and emit a victorious cry when the wax surfaced. He would then test my hearing by retreating behind the dining-room table and whispering to me. If I heard the words he breathed across the table he would nod his head rapidly in a paroxysm of triumph at the success of the treatment. Once when my doctor uncle was away and I had an abscess in my throat, Dr. Gerber came to give me a shot. He was so nervous that he literally pranced around my exposed posterior like a besotted elf and drove his hypodermic three times into my behind before he found the right spot. Since then I have not been able to look him in the eye without becoming convulsed, but in the light of my recent experiences I do manage to see him for what he is, a well-meaning and gracious little gentleman.

Just as I am about to help myself to the mikada the doorbell rings and there is a portentous bustle in the hall. The priests have arrived.

Always on these holy days, the Russian Orthodox priests pay a visit. There is usually a deacon and an archimandrite, both effectively robed and head-dressed, with either crosses or icons swinging on their chests, and a short service for the well-being of the family is conducted before one of the holy icons in the house. Usually those of us who do not belong to the Orthodox faith retreat to another room, and listen to the service in silence and with a distant respect. I hastily slice off a substantial chunk of the mikada and follow my mother and my Aunt Lida into the waiting-room with the modest Venus de Milo, where a few others have already gathered, anxious not to intrude upon a sacred ritual. The chants of the priests and the pungent odour of incense makes the ceremony densely mysterious and archaic, and I never fail to feel alien and somehow left out.

These religious ceremonies at my aunt's house fill me with a sense of loss, guilt and defiance. Since that memorable night in my middle teens when I lost my faith in God, I have alternated between atheism, agnosticism and fear of the God I had rejected. I agreed to confirmation in the Anglican Cathedral because of this fear. Later I knew myself for a hypocrite for the confirmation had failed to restore my faith. And since I lost my faith and have as yet found nothing with

53

which to replace it, I always feel at sea among all these people so earnestly devout, so deeply rooted in their beliefs. I feel at sea now with no bark to cling to. I also feel resentful.

Among those closeted in the waiting-room with us is Mr. Rezzini of fine-foods fame and his plump wife who is sporting a string of magnificent pearls. Mr. Rezzini is short, balding, rotund, always charming, jovial. He speaks Russian but has never lost his Italian accent. We have been to their apartment for dinner in an exclusive residential area of the French Concession. At these dinners the table settings are impressively formal and I quake lest I use the wrong cutlery, and the after-dinner conversation is stunningly boring, but the food is always so good that these drawbacks seem minimal. Every Easter the Rezzinis send me the most enormous chocolate egg I have ever seen. These eggs are as big as footballs. They stand, half-opened, on a sturdy chocolate base, and are filled to the brim with assorted chocolates each wrapped in ritzy, colourful foil. Tied with magnificent ribbons and finished off with enormous bows, they are the wonder of the neighbourhood, and at Easter I always suddenly become very popular. At this point in time Mr. Rezzini has not yet perpetrated the folly that will earn him the scorn of all his righteous friends. He chuckles at the scarf draped round the Venus.

When the ceremony is over and my doctor uncle and his house duly blessed, the priests settle in for refreshments, served by my aunt herself. My Aunt Lida, the aunt who was brought out of the Soviet Union, looks on with an ironic twist to her lips. She is skeptical of the priests and has retained her Lutheran faith. My Uncle Ernest, unattached to any church but basically still Lutheran too, feels at ease with the priests, as he does with everyone, and chats and jokes with them, to the consternation of Maria Mikhailovna, his wife, who adheres to the Orthodox faith and feels that the priests should be treated with more reverence. But even

54

Aunt Lida's skepticism and Uncle Ernest's light approach to the representatives of the church do not obviate the fact that they both accept religion as a basic rule of life. Nowhere here will I find exoneration for my secret fall from grace.

With the priests has arrived a woman called Elisaveta Nicholaevna Litvinova. She is the most impressive person I have ever seen. Tall and once undoubtedly startlingly beautiful, she wears a long black gown and a kokoshnik. A kokoshnik is a Russian ornamental head-dress worn in the old days by highborn ladies, especially on state occasions. Elisaveta Nicholaevna almost always wears her kokoshnik. It is black, embroidered with beads and pearls and supports a veil that falls down the back of her head to her shoulders. She is well-known in the streets, and people stare after her with forgivable curiosity. She always moves slowly, majestically, like a ship under full sail. She is the widow of a tea merchant and very wealthy, but she is also very religious and consorts with the priests and the elders of the Russian Orthodox Church, all of whom hold her in the highest regard. I run into her in the doorway of the waiting-room as I am hurrying to the dining-room to get some meringue-and-whipped-cream cake, and she asks after my health and then makes the sign of the cross over my head.

I experience mixed emotions. I am enchanted by her sheer force of personality but I also resent the blessing. It seems presumptuous. As Lutherans we do not make the sign of the cross over our friends and perhaps she should respect this. In addition her blessing stirs up the guilt in me so that I can scarcely handle it. I feel a mad urge to rush away from the house, from its religiosity, from the hold it has upon me. Then I steady myself and try to recognize the gesture as well-meant. I betake myself to the dining-room and the consolations of the meringue-and-cream cake.

A year or two later Elisaveta Nicholaevna lies dying in her apartment on Bubbling Well Road, close to the famous Café Federal, and Mother and I go to visit her. Her face is wasted and her hair, sparse, grey and lank, hangs loose. She holds a cross on her chest, her fingers resting on it lightly, long and thin and elegant. My mother stands close to her bedside but I hang back. There is the same mystique of religiosity about her that I have always felt. As always it fills me with guilt. As always I am half fascinated, half resentful.

Some time ago, in Vancouver, my cousin Nina saw the ghost of Elisaveta Nicholaevna standing at her bedroom door. She was dressed plainly, her hair grey. She stood for a few minutes, looking sad, then vanished. She still has a hold on us.

Back at the name's-day party, toward dinner-time I catch my mother glancing at the clock and I know that she is worrying about my father, but soon the doorbell rings yet again and he arrives. The same solicitous houseboy who snatched off my mother's hat and demolished her hairdo, divests him of his street clothes, and as he straightens his jacket and his tie I notice the nervous tick under his right eye that has been in evidence off and on ever since the guns were first heard in August. A surge of love gushes over me and I rush to throw my arms around him and to kiss him. Slightly bewildered, he greets my doctor uncle and then retreats to the "zakuska" table to which cold cuts and salads have now been added, inclines his head to the priests who have entrenched themselves beside it, and accepts a glass of vodka from my aunt.

Gradually the crowd thins out, the mere acquaintances and persons who are perhaps just patients and have only come to wish the doctor well, go their way, and we are left with the closer friends, those who stand second only to the family in the concentric rings of adults hemming in my young life. I hear the piano starting up in the living-room and after a few moments the voice of Tanya, the dentist's wife raised in song. I hurry to the living-room.

My aunt's living-room is enchanting and memorable. The furniture is a rich blue velvet and the carpet, also blue, thickly luxurious. I love to sit on the carpet and sink my fingers into its pile, although my aunt frowns at such conduct, unseemly in a young lady. There is a large basket of flowers on the piano, one of the many name's-day gifts, and several fine paintings, in gold, curlicued frames, hang from hooks attached to the cornice that runs around the room. Tanya is singing a melancholy song about evening bells, and then she sings one about snow blowing across Russia. My favourite is called "Monotonously Rings the Little Bell," and is about a horse-drawn buggy on a long road and the sad song of the driver. She gives voice to this one too, while the elders wipe their eyes surreptitiously with a fingertip or with little lace handkerchiefs. Tanya is renowned for her repertoire of Russian folk music. The dentist stands leaning against the wall, smoking a cigarette, looking enigmatic, his lethal black eyes slightly clouded.

The singing over, my Uncle Ernest, pink from festal cheer, blond hair ruffled, invites everyone back to the dining-room where he is about to propose a toast. Everyone's glass is filled and Uncle Ernest toasts my doctor uncle and wishes him many more name's-days to come with lots of food and drink and no more wars. "To the future," he cries, and everyone drinks. The protective circles of adults around me have secured my years to come.

And this is the moment when I experience the realization that will mark for me the dawn of a departure from the order of things as they exist around me. I see my parents and my relatives in a constrictive ring, moulding me, forming my opinions, guiding me with kindness and concern, and I see the outer ring of concurring friends, a strong supportive wall for these opinions, for this guidance. I see them with a clarity never to be erased from my mind. And I know what it was that I left behind in Hong Kong. I left freedom behind. With my sister as a friend rather than a mentor I experienced freedom for the first time. And that is what I desire above all things. I do not depreciate the care and concern that have been lavished upon me, I am grateful for them, but care and concern, and love itself, come with a price. It is only through freedom that I shall be able to find whatever it is that I'm looking for, whatever it was that challenged me on that night when I lost my childhood faith. I know I have arrived at a point at which my life will take a different direction. The goal is hazy, as is the path I shall take. I cannot even be sure that I am right, but the urge to break away, to set out, is irresistible.

Chapter Five

In Vancouver, in the attitudinizing eighties, I visit my aunt and my cousin Nina in their condo. My aunt has been ailing, but she gives my solicitude a characteristic brush-off. "I'm fine," she says, "Nina's always fussing." She has just received a letter from Tanya. Tanya and her dentist with the irresistible eyes emigrated to the States after the communist takeover of Shanghai.

"What a kook he was," Nina says, "with his radios and his fish and those crazy bees."

"He had hives opening out onto Avenue Joffre," I recall. "I was terrified sitting in that waiting-room with those bees buzzing in and out of every window."

"And then it turned out to be illegal in the Settlement," my aunt shakes her head at the folly of it all.

"So he got the goat," Nina says.

A little spurt of laughter escapes my aunt and we laugh with her. I remember that goat. I met the goat and the dentist on a steep flight of stairs one day when I came for a filling. The goat was recalcitrant, the dentist furious. It was milking time. Goat milk was being touted, he was on a health-kick, it would sell. By that time he had lost most of his foreign clients and was forced to treat Chinese, which he considered beneath him.

Nina goes to make tea. "They are all gone," my aunt says, spreading out her hands in a gesture of loss. She falls into a reverie, gazing out at the greenery outside, her lower lip protruding. I think of the Rezzinis and Dr. Gerber and poor Nyuta whom China had made mad. She also emigrated to the States where she founded yet another home for cats, unsuccessfully, for the neighbours objected and the cats were removed. Someone gave her a canary. I think of all those adults who ringed me in my youth and who are now dead, or scattered the world over, and I remember the realization that came to me upon my uncle's memorable name's-day, that what I wanted above all was to escape from their ambience. I had decided that the first step toward the freedom I craved would be to find a job at the earliest opportunity, and, thanks to Mr. Law's excellent tuition, I managed to get one in the New Year with an American firm manufacturing pharmaceuticals for the Chinese market.

I see myself on that first day entering the building on Kiangse Road. The building is situated close to the smelly Soochow Creek. The Soochow Creek is an indescribably filthy, slow-moving mass of water that delineates the northern boundary of the International Settlement and joins the Whangpoo River at the point of the Garden Bridge. This bridge connects the southwest section of the city with the northeast section, the east end of my childhood. Hundreds of rag-tag boat people live on the Soochow Creek and a third die every year from pollution-related diseases. Its smell pervades the air around the office building, but after I have been in the office for a while I no longer notice the smell.

In the office I have a large, sunny room all to myself with a big desk and two typewriters set in the centre of the room each on its own table. They are a far cry from the creaky old Underwood on which I learned my skill. One typewriter is for letters, the other, much larger, for financial statements.

At the far end of the room is a fireplace that is never lit and in front of it a table with a hot-plate and a tea-kettle, a large tray with teacups and all the necessary paraphernalia for making tea, and a cookie tin with expensive imported biscuits. One of my duties is to make tea in the afternoon and take it around to the boss who has an office next to mine, and down the hall to the accounts department at the other end of the building. Halfway down the hall is a rather gloomy, windowless area, electrically lit, in which several Chinese clerks and salesmen are always busy at work. They are set apart from the corridor by an iron grill. I never make tea for them.

Right next to our office building and separated only by a narrow lane from the accounts department, is a brothel. I do not know this. In fact I do not even know exactly what a brothel is. The windows of the brothel are very close to the windows of the accounts department and when I take the tea in to that department, I sometimes see women in night-gowns walking around the rooms across the lane. I have no idea what they are doing in their nightgowns in the middle of the day, but fortunately I never ask. I notice that one or another of the men in the accounts department often stands by the windows looking out, and there is some banter and laughter that ceases when I enter. Once I catch a glimpse of one of the women bare to the waist. I am embarrassed and vaguely troubled, but as it doesn't concern me I put it out of my mind. I certainly never mention it to my parents.

The boss is a short, burly, middle-aged Britisher, with a red face and a bristly moustache. I don't like him very much. In the accounts department there is the chief accountant who is slight, with pale brown hair and a moustache like a smear of milk chocolate across his upper lip. He seems quite pleasant. There is also a younger man, a Eurasian, assistant to the chief accountant, who has thick, black oriental hair but large, brown European eyes. His skin is sallow, he is heavy-set and always has a pipe hanging out of the corner of his mouth.

In the room allotted to the Chinese employees, there is a young Chinese called Yang who wears extremely thick glasses that make his eyes look grotesque. Yang brings in the mail in the morning, picks up the tea-tray when I'm through with it and brings everything back fresh and clean and ready for the next day. He always nods and grins, and I like him a lot, but I am not supposed to hold conversations with the Chinese staff. There is also Tong, who is the head of the Chinese department and to whom I give my orders for office supplies. He is older, grave and polite. I like him best of all the staff but do not talk to him about anything except the supplies for the same reasons. I have no association with any of the other Chinese.

The basement of the building holds the manufacturing plant and is full of mysterious machines under the supervision of a White Russian chemist called Boukov. I see him seldom, but he seems kindly and capable. He has short, reddish hair that sticks up all over his head making him look exactly like a toy bear. Mr. Boukov is responsible for the manufacture of a strange-smelling white ointment that is advertised as having been specially produced for the sons of China, and small red pills that are supposed to cure kidney ailments. As I have neither skin nor kidney problems I have no opportunity to test the efficacy of these remedies.

I am good at my job and happy in it. Sometime in the spring two auditors appear in the accounts department. One of them is short, square-set and oldish, at least thirty, and so not very interesting. The other is young, tall and slim, with dark hair and very blue eyes. I feel shy when I go into a room full of men with my tray of cups and I hardly look at the auditors, let alone think of speaking to them.

Two of the swains have gone. They left for Britain during the Japanese hostilities, and my main swain now suggests that we join a group of four other young people to take lessons in ballroom dancing. Once we acquire this skill we can go to tea dances, much in vogue, and perhaps even dinner dances, although I'm not sure about those, for even though I'm now seventeen I'm still not allowed out at night with young men unchaperoned. I agree to join the dancing class.

My main swain has bought a car. He now has a job in the accounts office of one of the swanky British department stores. His car is a relic, a small four-seater. The driver's seat is damaged and every so often collapses, landing my main swain on his back, and I often have to haul him up again into a sitting position. This is disconcerting, but a car's a car. Easter is late this year, in May, and I need a new outfit. I have saved some money and I want something more elegant than homemade clothes and hand-me-downs, so I order a suit from a Chinese tailor for the holidays.

This tailor, recommended by a friend, is situated in a back lane off one of the streets in the French Concession. The entrance to the shop is guarded by mean-eyed wonks, dogs of an indeterminate ancestry. I'm terrified, but the tailor shouts at them and I go through. His workplace, comprising his cutting-tables, sewing-machines and ironing-boards with their charcoal-heated irons, is open-ended and housed under an extension of his main domicile. A small boy, wielding huge shears is cutting along a line chalked on a length of cloth. I am taken inside the house for measurements, where I am swamped in steam and the odour of cooking rice. His wife grins at me, showing two gold teeth, and small raven-haired children give me black-pebble stares. I wonder how my suit will turn out.

The suit turns out perfectly. It is a pale grey and has a tight skirt and a flared three-quarter length jacket. Very stylish. I buy a white satin blouse to go with it. It ties high at the neckline and has pearl buttons on the cuffs. I am delighted with my outfit. I feel very grown-up. I have been wearing silk stockings ever since I left school, and I now buy a pair of black patent-leather high-heeled shoes. The group wants to go to a tea dance on Easter Saturday.

My mother is displeased. She says it's a sin to go dancing during Holy Week. She asks me if I have forgotten that Jesus died on Good Friday. I say no, I haven't forgotten, but he didn't die on Saturday. She reminds me that Saturday is a day of mourning, a holy day. I ask her why she never goes to church herself if she is so religious. She purses her lips. I know there is no Lutheran church in a language she can understand and that I'm being unfair. I hug her. I promise to attend church on Good Friday and on Easter Sunday if she'll only let me go. She relents. Very well, she says, but no good will come of it. Mark my words, she says, shaking a finger at me. I'm relieved and delighted but her warning haunts me. I shut it out.

The tea dance on Saturday is held in a nightclub that also features afternoon functions. I have never been to a tea dance before. We sit at a small table covered with a dingy white cloth and there is a vase holding rather dusty artificial flowers set in the centre. Nothing looks very glamorous in the daylight. We order tea and cakes. The music strikes up and we pair off. We all feel very competent. I think I look very fetching in my new outfit, I love the pearl buttons on my cuffs. I notice a number of women, mostly Chinese, sitting in a row at one side of the dance hall. These are the hostesses who dance for a fee with unaccompanied men. I feel sorry for them, they look under-nourished and pimply. I mention this to my swain. He shrugs. They're just a bunch of whores, he says. What d'you mean? I exclaim. Well *of course,* he says, what did you think? He laughs unpleasantly. *Of course* I knew *that,* I say loftily, but you could be *sorry* for them. I think his attitude is unkind and arrogant. I'm angry at myself for betraying my ignorance and at him for laughing. Actually I'm not even certain what the word "whore" means, and how is it spelt, I wonder. I think of the women across the lane from my office. I feel distanced from him and remind myself to hold my tongue.

After the tea dance my main swain sees me home. Just as I

am getting out of his car, a young boy, the bane of the neighbourhood, throws a well-aimed tomato at me. It's large and juicy and lands with considerable force just by my right lapel. I say a hurried farewell to my swain and rush into the house to sponge it off. To my horror a large stain remains. I can see the suit will have to be cleaned but the dry-cleaning stores will not open till Tuesday. I will have to go to the Easter Sunday service in my old suit. My mother doesn't say I told you so, but the words thunder in my head anyway. I burst into tears. My mother says she has a bunch of artificial violets that I could wear pinned over the stain, but it isn't the same, the violets look old-fashioned.

The following week we all attend our last dancing lesson for the year. My swain often drives the girls home, but toward the end of the lesson he says he wants me to himself this evening. He doesn't understand why I have to drag the whole crowd with me wherever I go. He and I could go somewhere for cake and coffee. Strangely I become panic-stricken. I tell him that my parents don't like me staying out late and if he doesn't give the other girls a ride I shan't go with him either. He becomes obstinate. He says the girls in the group are a pain in the neck, they're always tripping over his feet—maybe theirs are too big, he says, guffawing. I'm furious at this totally unwarranted criticism and when the lesson is over I march off in a huff and catch a bus.

We have split up. I feel rather sad and comfort myself with the thought that I'm well rid of such a rude and mind-less fellow. In fact the whole group breaks up and I'm left to my own resources. I think of my mother's warning. Could God really be so petty and vengeful? After all I did attend both services at Easter. But my world has fallen apart.

This year I don't join the Cathedral Tennis Club but instead apply to the BAT Club for membership. This is the fond name for the British American Tobacco Company and their club is open to anyone who can afford the fees. It's quite expensive but I feel rich with my pay coming in each month. At work I am told that during the months of July and August the office will be open from eight to one and in the afternoons I will be free. This suits me well. I take my lunch with me and go straight to the tennis club after work. I spend long afternoons on the Race Course, which is far cooler than the sweltering city.

The Race Course is a fine retreat for sports-minded people. In the very centre of the expanse of grass stands the Shanghai Cricket Club, one of its few permanent buildings. I often walk by this fancy club. Built of red brick, it has a grandstand with broad shallow steps accommodating tables and chairs where members and friends can sit and enjoy refreshments while watching the endless cricket games. Beyond the cricket pitch there are tennis courts. I know that racial discrimination is practised at the Cricket Club, that Jews are never accepted for membership. Although I have no intention of attempting to join it I do wonder if they would also exclude Estonians, never mind emigrants. I resent the Britishness of the Cricket Club just as I resented certain snobbish British girls at school, but I have no objection to the fact that the only Chinese allowed on the Race Course are servants and ballboys.

At the BAT Club I meet Ingrid. She is Scandinavian, we are the same age and both have wonderful older sisters. Ingrid loves poetry and we often sit on the grass in the shade of the blue tennis screens reading our favourite poems to each other. We like Swinburne best. We have both been writing poetry secretly and Ingrid wants us to share our poems. This is not easy for my guarded nature, but she is so eager I have to agree. She reads with passion. Her reading transfigures the grass and the sky. I float above the earth. Ingrid burns, phosphorus-bright.

Once I tell Ingrid about the time I woke up in the middle of the night to find I had lost my belief in God. This makes another bond between us as Ingrid has never been able to believe in anything at all. It would be comforting, she says, to be able to believe, like when you were a kid and took everything for granted. She says she feels there's a big hole in her chest. I know just how she feels. She tells me her sister is a theosophist and that they have regular meetings that she sometimes attends, but so far it hasn't helped her. I have no idea what a theosophist is but I don't ask immediately. I will find out in my own time.

When Ingrid is unable to come I play with the marker during the early part of the afternoon when there are very few people at the club. As the marker is Chinese I never speak to him except to ask him to play.

To my surprise my main swain also joins our club. This bothers me because I'm not eager to resume our relationship. He introduces Ingrid and me to another young man called Reggie possibly hoping to pair Ingrid with him. Reggie is short and slight and not very attractive. Ingrid is not at all keen on Reggie and we try to avoid them both, retreating behind the screens when they appear and giggling a lot, but one day Reggie brings a friend to the club.

I recognize Reggie's friend to be the young auditor who came to my office in the spring, the one with the very blue eyes.

The young auditor and my main swain pair off in a singles and the young auditor wins. Ingrid and I sit on the grass by the blue screens and giggle.

Visiting days at the club are limited, but whenever possible the young auditor comes to the club with Reggie. On those days we played mixed doubles. Ingrid thinks the young auditor is very handsome but I'm cautious. When we play doubles I usually happen to play with the auditor. I hope Ingrid and my main swain will fall in love, but they don't.

In the early fall my swain tells me that the Reverend Ottewell, who is the assistant to the Dean of the Anglican Cathedral, is arranging a series of discussions at the church. He says the discussions are quite interesting, lots of young people attend and afterwards there's a whole lot of good grub and we can play table tennis in the church hall. Ingrid has temporarily disappeared from the city. Her father has business that often calls him away. I miss her a great deal so I agree to go to the discussions.

I go to the first session with Grace Arlington and when we arrive I find that the handsome young auditor is there too. I'm surprised because I have never seen him at church. After the discussion I am initiated into the mysteries of table tennis. I find I am quite good at it. The handsome young auditor is *very* good. He beats my main swain again.

I begin to attend the discussions regularly. I discover that the handsome young auditor is of a radical turn of mind. He believes in free love, though I'm not exactly sure as to what that means, and don't dare ask, and he doesn't believe in God. He says he's an agnostic. This is a new word to me but as I listen carefully to the talk I gather than an agnostic is a person who holds the view that no-one can really know what the universe is all about, or whether there is a God. I doubt if I can go along with all the opinions of the handsome young auditor, but I remember my own fall from grace and I can relate to his view in this regard. I don't say anything as it seems somehow disloyal to the Reverend Ottewell whom I have known for so long but the Reverend Ottewell doesn't appear to be in the least daunted by the young auditor's opinions.

One evening I come home from a meeting and find my parents toasting one another. I stare at them, this is such an unusual sight. They pour out a glass of wine for me too and they tell me that an agreement was signed in Munich between Mr. Chamberlain and Adolf Hitler and that there won't be any war. Mr. Chamberlain has said that there will be "peace in our time." As I wasn't aware that the world was in jeopardy I am bemused, but join in their celebration anyway.

One evening when my main swain's car has broken down

and he does not appear at the discussion session, the handsome young auditor offers to see me home. His name is George and he is British.

We ride on the top storey of the double-decker bus and talk about the evening just past. He is now quite shy and at first not as outspoken as he generally is at the discussions. As the bus moves along we look out at the road and at all those Chinese refugees who have made temporary shelters in disused doorways and unfrequented alleys and have lived there ever since the Japanese destroyed their homes. No-one is attempting any reconstruction or rehabilitation, it is too vast a job. They live miserably and die without anyone caring. On my way to the office I pass by many such groups. I often see that one of the refugees has died. The dead person lies under the matting instead of on it. Sometimes dark purple limbs protrude. I cross the street whenever I see this. I am afraid of the refugees. They are spreading typhus throughout the city and we all wear little bags full of camphor pinned to our underwear, which is supposed to discourage lice. The coffers of the charity organizations empty faster than they can be filled. The handsome young auditor shakes his head and says the poor should not have to depend on charity and the whims of the rich. There should be a better answer. He asks me what I think of Mao Tse-tung. His eyes are startlingly blue.

I have no idea what I should think of Mao Tse-tung. The fact is that I never think of Mao Tse-tung at all. I have certainly heard of him, and of Yuan Shi-kai and of Sun Yat-sen and Chiang Kai-shek, but their individual views and their positions in the political arena are somewhat vague to me. I can see that it would not be politic to admit to ignorance of this kind in the company of this young man. I am tongue-tied. I can't get much past the astonishing blue of his eyes.

But I have to say something. At least I do know that Mao Tse-tung is a communist of sorts. I say I believe the communists are terrorizing the peasants and taking away their livelihood. Our servant, Ah Foh, whose family is in the country, is my source of information.

It's the wrong thing to say. The handsome young auditor replies, very politely, that according to *his* information the communists pay for everything they take for their armies. They want the peasants on their side, he says, so why should they rob them? This seems to make sense but I have been brought up to condemn communists under all circumstances. The handsome young auditor says that, in the style of Robin Hood, the communists are only taking away the ill-gotten wealth of the landlords and giving the land back to the peasants. He reminds me that millions of peasants die of famines every year and the government doesn't do anything about it. Mao Tse-tung is trying to do something. Mao Tse-tung is changing the history of China. Have I read *Red Star Over China* by Edgar Snow? he asks. The young auditor has overcome his bout of shyness.

Needless to say I have not only never read *Red Star Over China* but have never heard of Edgar Snow. The radical turn of mind of this young man is very disturbing. I have never met anyone who has had a good word to say for the communists. My swains knew as little as I did about communists, politics and the history of China, and cared even less. Neither Grace Arlington nor my passionate new friend, Ingrid, gives a moment's thought to anything like that. I feel on very shaky ground and wish that I had carried out my resolve to learn more about China when I returned from my Peking holiday.

I try again. I point out that the communists did wicked things in Russia. Surely I know, says the handsome young auditor, that the Tsarist government itself was corrupt. Oppressed people anywhere will rise up because they have nothing to lose. My mind is whirling. Can I let this young man know of my emigrant connections? He tells me that he himself is a socialist, like George Bernard Shaw. Do I know the difference between socialists and communists? he asks.

To my distinct relief we reach my bus stop.

But when we get off the bus he asks me where I live. It is evident that he plans to walk me home. Alarm bells ring. I say I can get there on my own. I'm used to walking alone at night, I say.

He doesn't seem to have heard and saunters along beside me. I ask him where he lives and he says he lives on Rue du Consulat, near the Bund. I am astonished for this locality is at the other end of town, not too far from the Cathedral we have just left. He has done all this travelling just to see me home! I take heart. I tell him ahead of time that I live in a horrible house and I make it sound worse than it is so that when he sees it he won't be too shocked. He asks me if I have been keeping track of the Spanish Civil War.

My knowledge of the war in Spain is less than my knowledge of Mao Tse-tung, but I don't let on. Off and on, I say, but I don't fool him. As we walk along past the terrace houses on my embarrassing street, he tells me the details of the Spanish Civil War. I notice that his legs are very long and that he takes one stride to my two steps as I trip along in my high-heeled shoes.

When we come to the lane that leads to my house I hesitate, but he marches straight on. As it is late evening the garbage container at the entrance has started to overflow and there is a sour smell. I feel like dying but my young auditor asks me if I like classical music. For the first time in my life I'm glad to see my own front door.

I do not ask him in but say that maybe I'll see him at the next discussion group. He says he will be there for sure.

My head is spinning. If I'm to see this serious young man again I shall have to pick up a lot of general information. I did not know that one could have a fly-paper memory, go through school at the head of the class, pass the Cambridge entrance exams with honours and know so little. Maybe this young man will never speak to me again.

Chapter Six

We are now well into fall. My tan is still attractive for summers in Shanghai linger on into September and even October gets its share of fine weather. My figure is slim and firm, my legs well-shaped, the summer of constant exercise has paid off well. I am somewhat vain and think I look pretty good, and feel even better. But one day, to my alarm and distress, my boss puts his arm around me. I wriggle away.

Over the following weeks my boss makes more passes at me. I evade him. I would like to avoid him altogether but of course that's impossible. I don't know what to make of it. I'm sure he must be married and at his age he certainly can't be in love with me. Why would he be doing this? Is it something to do with my emigrant status? I'm sadly confused. I have never seen older men in my family or among our friends making passes at young women. I'm also embarrassed and I'm more embarrassed for him than for myself. It seems to me that he is making a big fool of himself. As I think about it, fear enters into the picture—I don't want to lose my job. The money is very important to me and to my parents, but if he continues in this way I might have to leave. And in that case what would I say to my parents? I would be shamed beyond words. They would be angry and might wonder whether I had encouraged him in some way. They might even accuse me of being loose and wayward like the girls in some of the books I have been reading who have, quite mysteriously, for the books are unexplicit, found themselves in the family way. I don't exactly know what one has to do to get in the family way. Can a kiss do it? I doubt it. I wonder about the Virgin Mary.

Or else, think I, my parents might suspect, ah how wrongly, that my work wasn't good and I was fired and am now making up this outrageous story. Could they think that of me when I have always done so well? I am caught in a dilemma because of this truly silly old man. I think of my mother's warning about Holy Week and it feels like a curse. Everything has taken a downturn since my Easter Sunday tea dance. Even my encounter with the handsome young auditor has left me feeling ignorant and unsure of myself. I feel nostalgic for the carefree summer of the swains.

Still, life is not without its interests and diversions even though the tennis season is over. In addition to the church discussion group I join the Foreign YMCA. As there is no YWCA, the YMCA serves as a mixed club and is the central meeting place for the youth of the city, particularly in the fall and winter months. It is situated opposite the Race Course on the ritzy stretch of Bubbling Well Road close to the new Grand Theatre and the even newer Park Hotel that has a glass dancing-floor and a roof through which you can see the stars. The Foreign YMCA is well equipped. There are gyms and a large swimming-pool, bowling alleys and an auditorium that is used for dances, amateur theatricals and debates. Our favourite place is the coffee shop where we love to congregate and drink tea, or the newly popular and more daring coffee, usually drunk only at breakfast, or, in the more fashionable homes, in the evening after dinner, and eat huge slices of their famous devil's food cake. I join a volleyball team and the debating society.

The debates are held in the evening and I am chaperoned by my sister and her husband. They have acquired a new friend called Ted Atkins who is older than they are and has many radical ideas, somewhat like my young auditor. My sister doesn't approve of these, but Ted Atkins is greatly taken with her, indeed she's very pretty, and she feels flattered. I understand, vaguely, that he has a wife somewhere, but I never meet her.

My sister who has always conscientiously guided me through my early years, approves of my attendance at the debates because she feels I need to improve my general knowledge and to widen my horizons. Of course, as always, she is right. Although my father has tried to open my mind to the joys of knowledge and speculation, I have not yet learned to formulate opinions of my own. My bout with my conscience when I lost my faith has not, as yet, resulted in anything constructive. Doubts and fears plague my mind from time to time, but I don't face them squarely as I have little ammunition to fight the front of organized religion and its attendant mores. Now I attend sessions at which people present well-considered opinions with clarity and precision. I am lost in admiration. I recognize that the Reverend Ottewell is trying to do something along these lines at our church discussions, but we are far too ignorant and confused in our thinking to offer anything of value, although my friend, the young auditor with the blue eyes, argues convincingly enough with the Reverend.

I am not surprised to see my auditor at the debates as well. He stands up once or twice to speak and I marvel at his courage, and then one evening when a subject particularly impassions me, I suddenly gather up my own courage, get shakily to my feet, and make a contribution too. I sit down, breathless, to an unexpected round of applause. Not every speaker is thus applauded. I am immediately filled with self-approbation. If I didn't make the Shakespearian stage after my success at school as Petruchio in *The Taming of the Shrew*, I can at least become a famous public speaker.

Ted Atkins encourages my sudden spearhead into public life. He declares that I could lead a debate if I set my mind to it. There will be a debate in the New Year on a subject I will be able to handle. The proposition for this debate, "That Women Dress for Men" interests me. I agree to lead the opposition.

I give a lot of thought to this subject. It is the first time in my life that I have actually given enough thought to any subject to be able to present coherent views of my own. I am excited and proud, even though it is not a subject as important as the Spanish Civil War.

Ted Atkins and I work together on my presentation. To Ted's delight he discovers my flypaper memory. I memorize the entire text of my speech.

In the meantime, back at the office, my boss, after a few more attempts at harassing me, takes the hint, so often given, and leaves me alone, but his manner becomes cool and distant. I prefer it that way though I'm worried he might fire me. He now demands absolute perfection from me in my work and objects to the smallest erasure, the slightest breach in punctuation. I begin to deliver perfection time after time, but even so at Christmas he does not give me the bonus I had been promised. I am too proud to ask for it. I cry a bit on my way home on the bus. I know I have earned that bonus.

This unfair deprivation is driven from my mind by the resumption of the debating sessions after the holidays. On the evening of my debate I am very nervous, but the moment I get up to speak I feel in control of myself and of the audience, much as I did on the stage at school. The evening is a great success and I am asked to lead another debate in the near future, the proposition being "That women should not invade the realms of men." I shall oppose this.

Ted Atkins offers to assist me again but my mother has become very anxious about him. She warns me that he is much older than I am and not suitable to have as a friend. I assure her that he is by no means interested in me (he hasn't made a single pass) and is far more interested in my sister, and besides that he is married. This makes her more anxious than ever. As I have already learned a great deal from my first debate in regard to marshalling my facts and disciplining my thoughts, I don't need as much help, so I decide to ease my mother's mind and do it on my own. This is also far more satisfactory to my ego, but I am glad I have not told my mother about my boss.

My second debate is even more successful than the first.

There are 500 people assembled in the YMCA auditorium and I win hands down. I do not know it, nor do I have a term for it, but I am a natural feminist and am following in the footsteps of my Aunt Lena who became a nurse in the face of an indignant father's opposition. The debate is reported in the local press and I become a minor celebrity. Several young men become attentive and my sudden popularity goes to my head. I experience a resurgence of the summer of the swains, except that now I am not quite as innocent, not as easily enchanted. The handsome young auditor is among the interested young men, but he keeps his distance. I am giddy with success. I see him watching me when we gather in the coffee shop for our refreshments, and his eyes are hooded when he looks at the other young men in our group. As for my main swain, he leaves me severely alone. I have given up going to the church discussion group. I do not see him at all, nor think of him.

A dark-skinned young man called Lewis Wood, also an acquaintance of my sister, wants to take me out. He comes with her and her husband to our house on Victory Terrace. He is swarthily good-looking, very intelligent and has charming manners, but to my surprise my father is extremely upset by the attentions of this young man. He says Lewis Wood has negroid blood. This is the first time to my knowledge that my father has shown racial prejudice. My sister says she thinks he is Celtic and she has heard that people with Celtic backgrounds are sometimes rather swarthy. My father says he has seen the palms of his hands, and they are very pink. That is a sure sign of the negroid strain. My father says that if I married him I could have black children. He takes me aside and speaks to me about this very seriously. He says that the black strain can reappear after several generations.

I remind my father that, far from marrying Lewis, I have not as yet even gone out with him. I am surprised and a bit intimidated by my usually mild father's impassioned speech

75

about my possible black children. His face has reddened and the tip of his nose has turned white. His tic has appeared. He looks unwell. I assure him that I do not intend to marry Lewis Wood and if it will please him I shall not even go out with Lewis.

At night I think about having black children. It's not a welcome thought. I've never seen a negro except on the screen. I certainly have nothing against negroes, they seldom enter my mind, but I can't help thinking that in all honesty I probably wouldn't like to have a child so different from myself.

My sister discovers that Lewis Wood has a Chinese mistress whom he keeps in one of the hotels. This is shocking news indeed and my father feels justified in his passionate outburst, although I can't see what keeping a mistress has to do with possibly being black. I was not particularly taken with Lewis Wood anyway, so I don't care one way or the other, but the thought of the black children continues to haunt me. In some curious way I feel guilty that I might not want them. Surely if they were my own I'd love them anyway. This thought comforts me. Certainly the black children I have seen on the screen were absolutely adorable.

Another new admirer is called Thomas Tompkins. Pale, with blond hair plastered to his skull, he is quiet and earnest and clever too, although I suspect he rather fancies himself. He asks me out to dinner and a late movie, and to my surprise my mother lets me go. We ride in a taxi, which is a new experience for me, except for the taxis we took on our holiday in the north, but it seems extravagant to take a taxi just to a restaurant. During the evening he asks me if I belong to a church. Yes indeed, I say, I belong to the Anglican Church. He tells me he's a Quaker. I have never heard of Quakers. Although I try to disguise my ignorance he can see through me and enlightens me. He explains that Quakers do not have churches but meeting-houses, and that there is no service such as we have in our Cathedral. They sit in silence, he says, until someone is moved to speak. There's plenty of time for meditation and for the spirit of God to purify your soul. This creates true sincerity, he says. I think it would create true boredom, but refrain from saying anything. I half wonder whether he's making fun of me, testing my credulity, a religious practice like that seems so unlikely to my ritual-oriented mind. On the way home, in another taxi, the earnest young Quaker clasps me in his arms and kisses me passionately and wetly. I never go out with him again. I think that children as pale as Thomas Tompkins, like under-done pancakes, would be far less desirable than cute little black children. He writes me sad poems which he mails to me at work.

At this time a very curious event takes place. We hear that a certain Dr. Bookbinder is coming to town. He is a world-renowned psychic, a telepathist and hypnotist and will give a lecture with demonstrations in the gymnasium of the Russian Sokol Sports Centre. Everyone is urbanely skeptical and primitively excited and we all go to hear him.

The hall is crowded. Dr. Bookbinder briefly reviews the psychic sciences and then gives us demonstrations of his hypnotic skill. I am fascinated but deeply mistrustful. I feel that the subjects may have been primed or are playing up to the famous man. After a break for refreshments the Doctor asks for volunteers for a demonstration of telepathy. My curiosity propels me out of my seat and I offer my co-operation. Dr. Bookbinder gives me a small pin and asks me to place it wherever I choose. His eyes are bandaged and he is led out of the gym. I look around and see a basketball net at the back of the hall. I walk over and stick the pin in the net-ting.

Dr. Bookbinder is brought back into the hall. He now asks me to walk behind him and, within the confines of my mind, to direct him to the pin. We set out down the left aisle, turn right and walk across the back of the hall toward the net. Although his response to my unvoiced direction is quite remarkable, I am still suspicious. There has to be a trick here somewhere. Following my directions Dr. Bookbinder finds the post. The net hangs above his head. Suddenly panic fills me. I have forgotten the exact spot where I have placed the pin. My mind goes blank.

It is then that Dr. Bookbinder utters the words that shall echo forever through the nullifidian tunnels of my mind.

"You have stopped thinking," says Dr. Bookbinder.

I ponder on this extraordinary proof of his ability for weeks. I carry this small jewel of absolute knowledge in my heart for the rest of my life.

The auditors come to the office again. I am not so shy now that I know the young auditor quite well. Everyone is very busy with the year-end reports and my boss is cross and once again demands perfection in everything I do. He warns me that I cannot have a single erasure on the balance sheet. My fingers actually shake as I type the last few figures. Once more I deliver perfection and once more it is not appreciated. When the year-end rush is over the auditors leave, and things become more relaxed. One day the accountant comes into my office and brings me a book. He says he has heard of my success at the YMCA debates and thinks I might be interested in reading this book. It's called *The Life and Loves of Frank Harris.*

I thank him and take the book home. I start to read it that night in bed, and I'm shocked and ashamed. I realize it is not a book I should have brought home. If my parents find out about this book and who gave it to me they will insist on my leaving my job. I have become dependent upon the money and although my relationship with my boss is not of the best I feel I am handling it satisfactorily. I can't imagine what the accountant could have been thinking of. I hide the book and smuggle it out of the house the next morning. In the office I put the book away in a desk drawer. I don't know what to do with it. I'm too embarrassed to give it back to the accountant. When I take the tea into the accounts office, I don't meet his eyes. I hate him for doing such a mean thing to me. Is he punishing me for the opinions I expressed at the debate? One of the things I said was that I thought women should have positions of greater authority in offices. The book remains in my drawer and I remain hurt and puzzled.

Neither of my parents come to the debates, my mother because of her poor English and my father because, except for his work, he is rapidly becoming a recluse. But they are supportive and proud and my mother likes to go to the YMCA to watch me play volleyball and to take tea in the coffee shop. The Y always echoes with activity and high spirits, and is invariably full of people, all of which she enjoys. I introduce her to my friends and because I am beginning to feel more secure in my own strengths, I am no longer so embarrassed at her English. I also notice that her poor English doesn't disturb the young men who are interested in me. They are polite and defer to her. She has started to treat me more as an adult, as an equal. Over tea we gossip and exchange views as we never seem to do at home, perhaps because I'm out so much and she's tired in the evening, or perhaps she feels more at ease chatting when my father isn't there.

She illuminates me in regard to various happenings pertaining to our relatives and our emigrant friends. Upon one occasion she tells me that Maria Mikhailovna, my Uncle Ernest's wife, is ill, although it's a secret as the illness is tuberculosis and not to be talked about. My doctor uncle has strongly recommended a sanatorium, but Maria Mikhailovna refuses even to consider it. My father thinks she has had the disease for a long time and that it accounted for her erratic behaviour in the past. He has always suspected something of the sort. There is no cure for tuberculosis except rest and nourishment. A sense of foreboding fills me, but I remember that my sister's husband was cured of the same illness by going to a sanatorium and I hope Maria Mikhailovna takes the same sensible course. My mother says she won't do that because she's afraid Uncle Ernest might get involved with someone else while she's away. This seems bizarre to me, no-one we know has ever done such a thing. And then, uneasily, I think of my boss.

Upon another occasion she tells me that a Russian friend of hers, one Katusha, who has been living in sin to the discomfiture of the community, informed her the other day that her man has asked her to marry him. This Katusha comes regularly to have lunch with my mother under the pretext of using her sewing-machine for some mysterious garments she never seems to complete. She has fuzzy, pale-red hair and a gentle face and always asks me the same two questions, how I am doing at work and if I have seen my cousin Nina recently. Despite the fact that Katusha is viewed askance by the community for living with this man unblessed by holy matrimony, my mother seems to enjoy her company and ignores the criticism of the neighbours, although she agrees that Katusha is quite foolish. I think Katusha is quite boring. Now my mother tells me that Katusha has flatly refused this offer of marriage. "Imagine that!" my mother exclaims.

"Why?" I ask, in true astonishment, for it seems so unlikely that this mild, pale person should take such a curious stand.

"She says she will lose her independence," my mother tells me. "That she will no longer be her own person. She must be mad." But somehow, in my estimation, Katusha rises like a diver from the depths of a pool.

One day, over a slice of apple pie, my mother imparts to me her anxiety about my father becoming such a recluse. "He never wants to go anywhere any more," she says censoriously. "He's either immersed in his books and magazines, or he's sleeping. He needs more and more sleep." And then she adds, "Never marry a man older than yourself. Men age much more quickly than women. Somehow they lose heart. None of my women friends have lost heart, but look at their husbands—at social gatherings they may be spruced up, but they're about as exciting as tree-stumps." She eats some of her pie and takes a few gulps of tea. "Do you know," she says with sudden fervour, "your father has had two soft-boiled eggs every single day for breakfast ever since I've known him. Can you imagine? Two soft-boiled eggs *every single day*!"

She's full of righteous indignation, but I burst out laughing and she joins me and cheers up, and we turn once more to the topic that interests both of us the most and which provides endless gossip for us over these teas, the young men who have been attentive to me, the blue-eyed auditor, Thomas Tompkins and Lewis Wood with the pink palms, and others less electrifying but whom my mother likes to dissect anyway. She had not been as worried as my father about Lewis Wood's ancestry, she quite liked him although she was as deliciously shocked as everyone else about the secret mistress. In regard to Thomas Tompkins, she has decided that although he seems totally trustworthy he is too starchy and unbending, and would not be suitable for a husband. She doesn't know how mistaken she is in regard to his trustworthiness and his starchiness and I do not enlighten her. And as for Ted Atkins, she repeats, I shouldn't even think of him. I assure her that I don't. He's truly old, probably all of 40. She says that a woman should never show her hand, she should always keep men guessing. I begin to realize how much she yearns for an atmosphere of fun and romance and how oppressive her life has been. I am interested to see that she seems to approve of my young auditor. I warn her that if he doesn't have pink palms he does have some very strange pink notions, but she says that most young men are idealists. They grow out of it, she says cheerfully.

My young auditor invites me to an afternoon show and we follow up with refreshments at a popular tea-room called DD's where they often play "Parlez moi d'amour," my very favourite love-song. It's very romantic. We order some meringue-and-cream cake for which DD's is famous. He asks me if I have heard the news. The British and the French have guaranteed the independence of Poland. It isn't clear to me why this is important. I say I have heard something about it and doesn't he think DD's makes the best cakes in town second only to the Café Federal? He says that since Germany invaded and annexed Austria a year ago and Bohemia and Moravia two weeks ago, and, so-to-speak, "accepted" the protectorate of Slovakia, Poland might be next. I see that I'm doomed to a political discussion so I jump in and remind him of the Munich Agreement but he says that he doesn't put much faith in that. You can't trust anyone like Adolf Hitler, he says. The significance of the various strategies in Europe is still vague to me and I decide that I must make a point of listening to the news every morning. Maybe I should even glance over the newspaper. It is 31 March, 1939.

As always I am awed at the earnestness of the young auditor. As I eat my cake and drink my tea I become ashamed of my flightiness. I try to rise above the blue of his eyes. I try to concentrate on the enigmatic character of Adolf Hitler and the dangers to Poland.

My young auditor pours more tea out of the Brown Betty teapot and I notice that his hands are strong and well-shaped. "Parlez moi d'amour" starts up and I suddenly think that my auditor is the nicest young man I have ever met. More than anything else I want him to have a good opinion of me. I vow to keep a tab on the fate of Poland, and I begin to think of him as George.

At the office the accountant brings some sheets of figures for me to type. As he explains the work I keep my eyes strictly on the sheets. He asks me if I have read the book he lent me. I say no, I haven't. I blush. I say I didn't much like it. He laughs. I gather up my courage and look up at him defiantly and he bends down and kisses me. On my lips. Then he leaves quickly. He does not take the book with him.

I am stunned. I had thought he was such a nice man when I first came, even though he did have that silly milk-chocolate moustache. But what with Frank Harris and his life and loves and now this, I am deeply disappointed and very angry. I am embarrassed for both the boss and the accountant. Once more I wonder if I should look for another job. I'm doing so well, not a single erasure on that balance sheet—six perfect copies—the pay is good, the place comfortable. Why should I be put in this predicament? I wonder whether I should speak to George about it. I think of the wives of the boss and the accountant and I'm appalled at the betrayal that has been perpetrated unbeknown to them. Is this what Maria Mikhailovna is afraid of? I can't believe it. My Uncle Ernest would never debase himself in this way. Are there many men like this? I wonder how I would feel if my husband went around kissing stenographers and lending them books about Frank Harris and his life and loves? My opinion of my boss has already sunk into the morass beneath the pavements of the city, and now that of the accountant tumbles after. I am very, very sad.

Chapter Seven

In May the tennis season opens on the Race Course. Ingrid is back and we both join the same club again. My main swain seems to have vanished completely. I have discovered that George is a member of the Shanghai Cricket Club. That he should be a member of such an exclusive club surprises me, for he does claim to be a socialist, but when I question him about it he says his father has been a member of the club for years and has been coaching him since he was little. I recognize that he too is a victim of a certain lifestyle, like Grace Arlington, and like I am a victim of my Victory Terrace environment and my cousin Nina of the environment of the Russian Orthodox Church and emigrant goodwill societies. I wonder how much any one of us can do about this victimization. While these matters spin around in my head George invites me to the Shanghai Cricket Club to watch him play. I go.

The large brick building of the Shanghai Cricket Club with its spacious grandstand, is very imposing and speaks of success and entrenchment. Here is the very heart of the British sporting community. Hegemony is as much part of the club as the bricks that form its walls and nobody gives it a thought. I give it a lot of thought. I don't feel at home like I do in the Foreign YMCA. My personal triumphs seem insignificant here among the powdered and hatted ladies and the men in their white flannel trousers and dashing blazers. My old feeling of inferiority relating to my emigrant status prickles all over me just under my skin. I could never bring my mother to this club.

George's sister is there and he introduces us. Then, somewhat to my dismay, he leaves me for the cricket pitch and I remain alone with his sister.

I have heard of this sister. I have heard that she is a very talented artist and I understand that she is in love with a relative of my girlfriend, Grace Arlington. I know Grace's relative by sight as he sings in the Cathedral choir. He is tall and distinguished. His hair is dark, long and wavy. When the choir enters the church and walks in procession toward the choir benches, he has a way of sweeping by the pews in his long black rustly gown, his head held high, which leaves all the girls breathless. Julian's parents, like Grace's, are very conservative and the accoutrements of religion are important to them. This family is somewhat less than delighted about Julian's interest in George's sister. Grace has told me, under cover of the utmost secrecy, that George's whole family is held in disfavour by the more conservative Britishers because of their radical views, and that Julian's parents are planning to send him back to England to deliver him from such an unsuitable relationship.

George's sister is a striking blonde and I think that she and Julian would look splendid together. I wonder why religion is always so troublesome. She is very gracious to me and orders tea and hot buttered buns. These refreshments are served by a Chinese boy, one of many who are kept hopping up and down the grandstand steps and successfully balance and deliver trays of glasses, bottles, tea essentials and goodies. Unlike most of the other women in the club, this beautiful girl does not wear a hat and her wonderful hair is spectacular in the sun.

As I talk to George's sister, I picture my friend Grace who goes to church with me so regularly, and her mother and father, pleasant and complacent, and I can see where this sister of George's could indeed be a worry to that family. Her quick, informed mind, her elegant posture, are threatening enough without her interest in Julian. The set of her head alone would be sufficient to scuttle that whole family so unprepared for any kind of challenge. I wonder why it is always the religionists who are afraid of the anti-religionists and not the other way around.

In between exchanges regarding art and literature and the immediate political scene at which latter I do quite well thanks to George's priming, we watch the game. It's very long and as I have no idea of the rules I find it quite tedious. George's sister does her best to enlighten me and tells me that George is a very good cricketer. I am impressed with the fact that he has never told me of this skill himself. To pass the time I eat a great many buttered buns.

The next day I relate everything to Ingrid and she tells me that she knows of George's sister and her problems with the dashing Julian, and in fact has even seen her in the company of her own older sister, the theosophist. It does seem a pity, she says, that religion is the cause of so much discord. She wonders if I'd like to come to one of her sister's theosophist meetings sometime. She admits that she finds philosophy hard to follow, but if we attended together we could talk about it later and maybe make some sense out of it. She'd love to find something to fill that hole in her chest. I say I would like that very much.

Our conversation is taking place in one of our favourite hideouts, a shallow ravine filled with grass behind the blue screens of the tennis club. We listen to the thud of balls against the screens, the twang of rackets, the shouts of the players. Faintly from afar we can hear the traffic on the out-skirts of the Race Course, along the major arteries of the city, the tooting of horns, the rumble of wheels. From above, the metallic eye of the sky stares down at us, unblinking. The smell of the grass around us is sweet and faintly dusty. Life stretches before us, endless and sweet as the grass and clear as the early Shanghai summer sky. Unlike George and his sister, Ingrid does not like to dwell upon the ominous turn of events in Europe, and neither do I. She is entranced with life and its marvels. Not for a moment will she consider the possibility that something could spoil the delicious blossoming of her youth. For her the future brims with tantalizing promises, with stores of unexplored trea-sures. I think of my friend Grace Arlington, with whom I still associate occasionally, and my even older and dearer friend Olga Sokoloff, whom I have shamefully neglected, and I see that staunch and reliable companions though they be, they are followers, followers of their churches, followers of the mores of their parents, of the societal patterns of their environments, but Ingrid is different. Ingrid flies ahead into the yet unveiled future, fearless and passionate. Grace is too polite to notice the garbage containers at the entrance to our lane, Olga shrugs them off, knowing her own lane holds similar eyesores, Ingrid simply never sees them.

Now, under the blue canopy of the sky, secluded from the

world by the screen of grass, I expect Ingrid to produce her copy of Swinburne and read yet again our favourite lines, but she does not do that. Ingrid rolls over in the grass, cups her heated face in her hands, looks up at me from under damp, wavy bangs, and tells me that something has happened to her.

I become apprehensive. Although my friendship with Ingrid is fervent, I have never opened up completely even to her. My old wariness is still extant. But Ingrid is far more flexible. I see that I am about to be the recipient of a truly momentous confidence. I'm not sure I want the responsibility. My heart draws in upon itself, sends out alerts, but to no avail.

Ingrid tells me she has fallen in love. She has fallen in love with someone she met at the Y. This is the real thing, she says, this is for life. His name is Carl and he is German. He is vaguely familiar to me as are so many of the young people at the Y. She says there is to be a dance at the Y to which Carl wants to take her, but her parents insist on a foursome. She asks if George and I would go with them. She will make all the arrangements.

We go to the dance as a foursome. I can see that Ingrid is very much in love with Carl and I only hope he is equally taken with her. I know there are depths to Ingrid that I have not found in my other friends. Although Ingrid laughs often and indulges in giggling fits as silly as those of any other teenager, this levity in her case is a cover-up for something else. It's a cover-up for the passion Ingrid betrays when she reads poetry, a disguise for the depths of joy and sadness, sometimes indistinguishable from one another, from which her love of poetry springs, her desire for spiritual resolution. I recognize those depths in Ingrid because I am just beginning to recognize them in myself. It is at that level that enchantment lies and sometimes, perhaps, even a certain kind of madness.

I watch Ingrid and Carl dance and small, cold fingers

pluck at my heart. I try to throw off this unwelcome sensation, but whenever I see Ingrid passing on the dance floor in her tight-fitting black dress, her arms around Carl's neck, wrapt in an eighteen-year-old dream of romance, I feel the chill. I am never to forget Ingrid that night, her flushed face, her short, curling blond hair combed close to her head, slightly damp at her forehead, her eyes cloudy with love. Ingrid who expected life to be full of enchantment forever.

On the way home I ask George if he likes Ingrid, but he asks me if I've heard that the Poles have signed a protocol with France that promises them assistance from the French air force should they be attacked. I say I heard my father mention it. I ask him if he didn't think Ingrid seemed very much in love with Carl, and didn't she look really attractive in that black dress. He says, yes, she seems like a pleasant sort of girl, and do I know what such a protocol might *mean*? I say I guess the French would protect the Poles if someone attacked them. I feel a chill squiggle up in my chest, the same kind of chill I felt earlier when I saw the way Ingrid looked when she was dancing with the German Carl, but I shrug it off. I say that nobody would be dumb enough to go to war. It is 19 May, 1939.

Ingrid invites George and me to her sister's house for a theosophist meeting. I agree to go but inwardly I panic. I have found out nothing about theosophy. I remember all those books on philosophers to which my father had hopefully introduced me years ago and how I had planned to read them all. I haven't read one. My fling with the swains batted all the sense out of my head, and later my success at the Y left me no time for quiet reflection. Now I go to my father for help.

My father is delighted to be approached on his favourite subject. I think he has been missing the times we used to spend together in my early teens lost in the marvels of his encyclopaedia, all twelve volumes of which he brought out of Russia at the expense of possibly more practical effects at the time of the revolution. I don't believe he has ever regretted his choice. The encyclopaedia has been his comfort and his salvation through all the hard years of exile.

He goes to the shelf holding the volumes and brings out the pertinent one. He sits down in his chair by the ugly silver arcola stove that provides heat to the radiators throughout the house in the winter, but is now, in the summer, dead and cold and depressing. He dampens his finger at his lips and finds the right page. Then he lights a cigarette and reads about theosophy. The encyclopaedia is in German, one of the five languages in which my father is fluent, so he has to translate the text for me. Theosophy, I learn, is the contemplation of divinity and its relationship to nature, its origin in large part being attributed to a German called Jacob Boehme who was born in the late sixteenth century. This Jacob Boehme, my father tells me, was a mystic. I am lost, and my father explains to me the difference between mysticism and religion.

Apparently it is possible to feel great affinity between yourself and the universe and the spiritual world without belonging to any organized form of religion. All the great religious leaders were mystics, but ordinary people needed something concrete to hold on to, so they invented gods and made pictures of them, images and icons, and symbols like crosses and magic charms, and introduced religious songs and ceremonies. The mystic's message, says my father, drawing on his cigarette, was then trapped in these forms, like a butterfly caught in lava—he has shown me a picture of this wonder in the encyclopaedia. My father becomes quite impassioned. I am surprised because I thought he approved of formal religion. Had he not suggested that confirmation by the church would be an advantage when I had doubts about everything associated with religion? I challenge him in regard to this.

He smiles wryly. Few people are blessed with the ability for abstract thought, he says, still fewer with the capacity to be religious leaders. For the ordinary person it's better to have some religious form than none at all. At least the church provides moral guidance. We can't all be mystics. I wonder if he's a mystic. I'm not sure if I know exactly what abstract thought is. And am I so ordinary? I certainly don't think so. I feel my own being as marvelous and unique.

He is eager to instruct me. He and I have grown somewhat apart since the days when he used to lie on his bed with his arms crossed behind his head making a black patch on the white enamel of the bed rail, and letting me into the secret imaginings of his mind. I'm sure he still pursues those imaginings, but I have been too busy confronting new experiences and he has not intruded. But he must have been feeling left out of my life. His eagerness is a kind of reproach in itself.

Now he says that with the way things are going in Europe we need philosophy more than we ever needed it before. He says a strange thing, he says that maybe God won't be enough.

When I see George next I tell him that I intend to become better read in philosophy. He suggests that I get a book called *The Story of Philosophy* by someone called Will Durant. This seems to me to be a good choice, certainly better than *The Life and Loves of Frank Harris*.

At the theosophist meeting people unlike those I am accustomed to meet in other areas of my life sit in a circle and give vent to weighty thoughts and speculations. It is intriguing but I realize that my knowledge in these matters is limited indeed and I deplore my ignorance in all its unfathomable depths. I glance at Ingrid, who rolls her eyes and clasps her head. Toward the end of the meeting my own head is spinning with new terms and definitions. It has certainly been instructive but when I am asked if I want to join the group I hesitate. There seem to be pledges to make. I'm not ready. I want to think all these things through for myself. I don't want to be trapped in a block of lava like the famous butterfly in the encyclopaedia.

When I get home to bed I begin once again to reconsider my adherence to the church. *Am* I an ordinary person? Do I need the church, the trappings of formal religion? Are they called trappings for nothing? All I want to do at this juncture is to learn as much as I can. I want to be able to discuss things in depth in the way the theosophists discussed them, and I would like to discuss them with some semblance of authority with the young man to whom I have become so attached. I want to be able to weigh and criticize, to be in a position to make judgements. This kind of thinking must become my way of life.

Whenever I recall that night some years ago when I suddenly knew I could never again unquestioningly believe in God, the vacuity of the universe fills me with the same enormous dread I felt then. I am unable to deal with this dread, so I suppress it, but it never leaves me. I think now that perhaps if I pursue this search for knowledge on which I have decided to embark, I will discover something that might fill this emptiness that threatens me so often beneath the layers of nonsense with which I fill my days—the emptiness that Ingrid describes as a hole in her chest. I make a resolution to devote time every evening to the study of philosophy. If I am not destined for the Shakespearian stage, nor perhaps for the public forum, I might still make my mark as a celebrated philosopher.

At the office the Eurasian assistant accountant brings in some work for me. He doesn't have much to say, but neither does he leave. He sucks on his pipe and rocks back and forth staring out of the window at the drab buildings opposite. I don't have much to say either, somehow I don't think that the elucidations of Will Durant or my aspirations to hit the heights of philosophy are going to make successful topics of conversation.

After a while he smooths down his hair and walks out of my room. I am left perplexed.

The assistant accountant takes to visiting me quite often. Sometimes he looks out of the window and sometimes he stands with his back to the window and puffs on his pipe. He regards me through the clouds of smoke in a melancholy way. I have become more at home with him and we talk about tennis and the growing tension in Europe. Now that I know all about the pacts with Poland and what they could mean I have no hesitation in airing political views, most of them George's. He never stays long.

One afternoon I come into my room and find the boss is looking through the drawers of my desk. He throws Frank Harris and his life and loves across the blotting-pad. What the hell am I doing with a book like that, he asks angrily. I am shocked. I have forgotten about the book being in my drawer. I say it isn't mine and I haven't read it. He asks me whose it is and I tell him. I hate implicating the accountant but I have no choice, I must stand up for myself. I see he is stunned in his turn. He picks it up and stomps out of the room. I can't imagine why he would be so angry. His own record isn't exactly lily-white. I also resent deeply his snooping around in my desk drawers. It constitutes an invasion of my privacy. It becomes clearer than ever to me that I shall have to look for another job and make the necessary explanations to my family. This latter thought fills me with distress. I burn at the unfairness of it all. I think I have made a friend in the assistant accountant and I wonder whether I should speak to him about it.

The boss goes off for a month's summer holiday and I'm delighted. I hope he never comes back. I sincerely hope I never see him again. Although I do not phrase the thought I know I wish he'd drop dead on his trip, but I'm afraid of God punishing me for having such a dreadful thought even though I can't really believe in God. It's all just too complicated.

One day there is an accident outside the office. A truck has hit a rickshaw. All the Chinese in the office line the windows in the corridor to see the excitement. The truck driver and the rickshaw coolie are yelling at each other. The rickshaw coolie wears a tattered blue shirt open to the waist and his patched pants are rolled up to just under his knees. He is barefooted, his toes are splayed, and his feet and legs are thickly covered with dust. He doesn't seem to be hurt but his carriage is damaged. The assistant accountant comes into my office to see the fracas the better from my window as the accident has happened at my end of the building.

A Sikh policeman has appeared on the scene and taken charge. He shouts and waves his baton. He brings it down on the back of the rickshaw coolie. The assistant accountant and I look out together at the enraged parties below. I'm feeling really sorry for the rickshaw coolie when suddenly the assistant accountant grabs hold of me and kisses me with shocking fervour. He smells of tobacco and sweat. I struggle out of his embrace, my head whirling. I thought he was my friend. He lets me go. He hits his forehead with the palm of his hand. "Christ!" he says, "Christ! I'm sorry." Then he leaves.

I sink into my office armchair. I have no idea what's going on. Am I the butt of some kind of joke? What are they all trying to do? Am *I* doing something wrong? If I am I can't imagine what it could be. My work is perfect and always presented on time. I never initiate conversations, I hardly ever look at anyone. It has to be something to do with my emigrant connections. They think they can take advantage of me because I am relatively unprotected like the Russian girls in the nightclubs about whom I have heard, though never seen. It is now obvious that I can't stay in this place any longer. I decide to go to George for help and advice.

This is tricky. I don't want to tell him the real reason for my sudden decision to leave. I'm afraid that he might get the wrong impression and the last thing I want to do is to lose his respect. When I speak to him I choose my words carefully. I want a change I say, I don't much care for the people at work. It's no lie, but I know I'm dissembling. Still, I don't dare tell the truth to anyone for fear that they may think I encourage those men, that I am "loose" in some unaccountable way. But I also don't want anyone to think I have failed at my job. My dilemma is truly distressing. George promises to make enquiries. I should also watch the papers, he says.

The days pass, hot and sultry. Even though I thought I was inured to the smell of the Soochow Creek its summer stench spreads through all the adjacent streets. It reaches even into the heart of downtown. On my way to work I see the miserable refugees sitting on their straw mattings, their terrible limbs exposed, searching for some relief from the heat. In the bus the sweat-soaked bodies of the passengers exude an almost unbearable odour. At home my father climbs the stairs to the roof garden of our house and looks out at the horizon hoping to see clouds that may presage a typhoon but the horizon is clear as a newly washed plate. He tears up bits of paper and lets them flutter down to the ground below to see if there's any wind. The papers float straight down.

I take dictation from the accountant in the accounts office, always in the presence of the assistant accountant. I am deeply embarrassed at first, but gradually the embarrassment fades leaving only anger and indignation. It is exasperating to think that men as silly as these should have the power to make me unhappy, and for no other reason than that I am a woman. The theories I put forward in my debate about women invading the realms of men are now blossoming into practice. I'm not going to be made miserable without fighting back. The decision I have made to leave gives me a heady feeling of power, freedom and independence. It will be sad to part with the job but I feel confident that I shall find a better one somewhere else. I'm a good worker, I have faith in myself and I have friends outside the office. I don't have to accept any nonsense from these men.

George and I are seeing each other steadily. I like him more than I can possibly say. We play tennis every day and on the weekends we go to shows or to the Y where George is teaching me duckpin bowling. Sometimes, if it's a very important game, I go to watch the cricket. Once I meet his father but as he is in some official capacity we don't have much time to get to know each other. I sit by myself at a little table and eat buttered buns with my tea. No-one talks to me.

In the newspapers and on the radio tension continues to build. Like the summer heat it closes in upon us relentlessly. It is no longer possible to ignore it.

I take refuge in poetry. A sad poignancy fills my days. I read Rupert Brooke and Wilfrid Owen and Siegfried Sassoon. My head rings with poetry—"And will there be such gladness where we walk today, tentative on the air, waiting? ..." "Like leaves lifted lightly by flurries of fall...." Ingrid and I compare notes on our boyfriends, mostly over the phone. We no longer see each other as often, but we know we are having parallel experiences that deepen our friendship. George is now my only companion as Carl is hers.

George and I seek out haunts in the hot dusty city, the grassy seclusions of our clubs or the parks heavy with trees and the perfume of tropical blooms. Sometimes a rare breeze brings with it the salty smell of the China Sea with its promise of freedom and adventure and the reminder of a world beyond our delta settlement. I sense that we are standing on the brink of some great disaster, but it is beyond our power, or the power of anyone, to do anything about it. My father listens to the radio with a new concentration. More and more German Jews arrive in Shanghai to take up a miserable residency in Hongkew, home of the famous Hongkew Market and reminiscent of my first meeting with Maria Mikhailovna and my lust for Japanese sweet and sour fish, Hongkew, always the shabby east end, and now mostly in ruins from the 1937 war and administered by the Japanese.

95

It is overrun by rats and mongrels, but the Jews crowd in, into the houses that have been spared. They can pay a little, not like the penniless Chinese refugees who fled the Japanese atrocities. Some of the British have started to return to England. I hear that my main swain has gone. I feel a brief stab of nostalgia—he has not said goodbye. As the summer progresses, hot, humid, full of mosquitoes and flies, watermelons and sugarcane, sweating rickshaw coolies and cholera among the poor uninoculated masses, prickly heat and hard cerulean skies, wide nights of brilliant stars and poignantly romantic moons, the apprehension grows. Foreshadowings of big changes hang over our daily lives. I am afraid and resentful. There has been too much violence in my life already.

On 1 September we hear Germany has invaded Poland, and suddenly all the speculations of the past months have become harsh reality. On 3 September we are having lunch at my sister's apartment when the news comes over the radio. Although I have been expecting it for the past two days, and, in fact, ever since the spring, it is like a great blow in my ribs. My sister's husband says, "That's the end, then, for all of us." My father has become extremely agitated. It is only 25 years since the last declaration of war. It occurs to me that my father is 67 years old.

Chapter Eight

This evening, in Vancouver, my aunt is sad. She is thinking about my uncle's gravesite. When my doctor uncle died in Shanghai soon after the war ended he was buried according to the ordinance of the Russian Orthodox faith. His resting place was in the Bubbling Well Cemetery, the cemetery reserved exclusively for foreigners. Some years after we emigrated to Canada we heard the cemetery was scheduled for demolition. The friend from whom my aunt heard this news told her that my uncle's remains could be moved to another graveyard on the outskirts of the city. Aunt Lena authorized this.

"He's all alone," she says sadly. "I can never forget that."

The Bubbling Well Cemetery was close to our Victory Terrace and in my younger years I walked past it often on my way to Olga Sokoloff's house. After sundown, on the way home, I ran past, intent on escaping the ghostly hands and faces my imagination conjured up. But in reality the cemetery was a place of great peace and melancholy beauty and the news of its demolition had been deeply distressing.

Over the years the thought of my uncle's grave in a distant, unknown site has often troubled me. Does his spirit still walk through that alien land? Does it know its loved ones did not leave it there willingly? His grave means nothing to the people who pass by there now. They cannot even read his name.

When my mother joined us in Canada after the war she brought a small black box with her. It contained my father's ashes. "I had no idea what to do with him," she said. "I couldn't just leave him there in that box." She kept it on a shelf in her cupboard and we got used to seeing it there. Kindness emanated from that box, goodwill. My father's ghost, having surely accompanied his ashes across the Pacific, lived compliantly in the cupboard. Did he chuckle when I turned on the television just as he had predicted so many years ago?

My mother told me that upon the night of my father's death he had called her to his bedside and told her that he felt absolutely wonderful, better than he had ever felt in his whole life. A few minutes later he died. "It was his reward," my mother said, "he was a righteous man."

Both these righteous, intelligent men were persecuted by

an angry world, innocent victims of the furies of others. They said little of their inner conflicts, unwilling to burden their loved ones. Gentle and well-meaning, they walk in my mind still, every quality and characteristic intact, and my aunt and I grieve for them both even though they have long passed the reach of our grief. I put my hand over hers as we sit side by side remembering them, remembering the war.

"We were in Europe when it all started," my aunt recalls. "Everything we had was in Shanghai. We didn't know if we'd ever get back." Even at this late date she shudders a little.

"Everything began to change so quickly in Shanghai," I say. "The British all wanted repatriation but their Government asked them to stay on, to keep the Empire going. They had enough trouble without a huge influx of colonials. George was told to apply to Singapore for service."

"By the time we came back in December your sister had left."

We sit together, hand in hand, two survivors. Sometimes I go to sit with my aunt when Nina is out although she stoutly denies her failing health. Once when she was actually confined to bed with a fever and I came to see her she started to scramble out. "What are you doing?" I cried. "I'm going to make you a cup of tea," she said.

The departure of my sister and her husband for his native New Zealand was one of the first blows dealt me by the war. During the Sino-Japanese hostilities in 1937 I had experienced mortal terror. I did not undergo anything like that at the start of the Second World War, but I suffered my first true loss. I cried the night my sister left and guiltily remembered how I had longed for her to get married so that I could have our shared room all to myself. Soon after that Grace Arlington left with her family. Even though she could not match Ingrid's glamour, she had been a true and staunch friend. Ingrid too had gone. My adolescence was coming to an end.

When the Soviet troops entered Poland in the middle of September, when the Soviets signed a Treaty of Friendship with the Germans, and Estonia, under a "mutual assistance pact" granted sea and air bases to the USSR, thus aligning herself with the Germans, apprehension entered my heart. When the Russians invaded Finland at the end of November apprehension turned to a nagging fear. My father looked grim. Politically the independence of Estonia meant everything to him. Estonians are proud people. He had been proud of this independence. He kept a picture of the general who had achieved it on his dresser. The liberation of the Baltic States had been the one positive result of the Russian Revolution. The mutual assistance pact was a step backward.

Although I too feared for the fate of Estonia and what this could mean to my much-touted Estonian sovereignty, this was not the main issue for me at that time. What caught my heart in a vice was the sudden fear that George and I might be arraigned on opposite sides of the field of battle. Could the slowly blossoming rapport between us be brought to an untimely end by forces entirely unrelated to us? I knew that this relationship with the serious, knowledgeable young auditor was the best thing that had ever happened to me. I was still somewhat giddy, my head filled with the triumphs of youth, unwilling to confront any fact of life that was not amenable, but in those moments when I could tranquilize the whirligig in my brain, I recognized our growing closeness as something of truly singular worth.

In addition, to my dismay, but hardly to my surprise, George now announced that he would offer his services to the Singapore defence force as suggested by the British government.

During our exile in Hong Kong in 1937 I had discovered a curious trait in my character. This was an ability during a period of adversity to shut out speculation and to retreat to an inner strongroom of my own making. Unknown to myself I had used this faculty at the age of twelve when my life had been overturned by adult mandates and I had escaped from further agonizing by engrossing myself in my father's extensive encyclopaedia. Upon George's announcement I found that I was putting my emotions on hold again.

George took and passed his medical examinations. I received the news stonily. He started to prepare for his departure. In my strongroom I read Swinburne, I relived the lighthearted summer days I had spent with Ingrid, I wrote poetry I did not know was often bad but that for brief periods revived the exhilaration I had felt then. I took my mother out to tea, I paid more careful attention than ever to my office work. I was building up barricades. And then the British Government announced that recruits were not going to be taken for Singapore after all. There wasn't enough equipment for them and those who had been among the first to be dispatched by the local office were returned to Shanghai. Instead of being sent to Singapore George was asked to report for patrol duty on British merchant-marine ships in the harbour. I emerged from my strongroom. I relaxed my vigilance.

Just before the outbreak of war George had obtained a job with the Shanghai Gas Company, a distinct improvement on the auditing firm. With the rejection from Singapore, he was now able to settle into this new job in good earnest, and arranged to do his duty on the ships at night. A small measure of stability entered our lives, even if only temporarily.

It wasn't long before we began to notice shortages in the city. Merchant-marine ships were not coming in as often as before. Those persons with their ears tuned to the future and their noses steeped in profit began to hoard commodities. Prices rose. Produce was still coming in regularly from the hinterland, but the hinterland was feeding three armies, the Chiang Kai-shek troops, the Communist revolutionaries and the army of the Japanese invaders. The coast cities took what was left.

In the middle of all this upheaval my efforts to find a new job were suddenly rewarded. I had never deviated from my decision to leave the pharmaceutical company and its amorous staff. Full of triumph and relief, ill-timed as it might have been, I served my notice to my boss. He stared at me, amazed.

I can't remember exactly how the conversation went, but it approximated something like this:

He asked me if I was leaving because I wanted more money.

I said no, that wasn't the reason. The pay was fine and I liked the job. I must have blushed at this point because he seemed to catch on, but he pressed me to state a reason.

I wasn't happy, I said. There were things I didn't like. He must know that.

He mused for a bit while I got more embarrassed and nervous, and angry at being forced to make explanations. Then he said most young women would be flattered to get some attention.

I said I wasn't one of them.

He said it wouldn't be much different anywhere else.

I remembered the opinions I had aired in that debate in the winter, the assertions I had made. I remembered I had won the debate. Had it only been talk? Now that I was face to face with an actual situation, would I stand my ground, make my position clear?

They weren't being fair, I said, my work was good. I had been hired to do that work, not for anything else.

I think I blushed again. It was not easy to fly in the face of behaviour and attitudes that seemed to be generally accepted in offices. I was trembling, my voice was unsteady. I was determined not to burst into tears and the indignation I had been suffering for so long came to my assistance. The power of the senior male over the female who was never senior and therefore totally helpless, was outrageous. This was harder than facing 500 people in a hushed expectant hall.

There were some painful moments when neither of us said anything. I remember hearing Yang rattling a tray of cups and saucers on his way to my room and the spasm of regret I felt. Somehow, here in my first job, I had failed. It was my first failure and it was infuriating because I knew it wasn't my fault. He broke the silence. He said he'd like me to stay. He said I was a good worker, that if I stayed I wouldn't be bothered. He asked me to reconsider.

He suddenly looked old and tired. I remember thinking that, how old and tired he looked, and how sad. He didn't insult me by offering me more pay, at least he knew better than that, but he had offered what I wanted.

I said I would think about it.

I thought very hard. I had fought a hard battle here and I had won. If I went elsewhere would it be the same all over again? Was he right about that? Or did he want to keep me because so many good English secretaries had been repatriated and it wouldn't be easy to find a replacement?

Perhaps. But I preferred to think that I was indeed a valuable worker and that he had recognized his foolishness. I preferred to think that my stand for the dignity of women—no one thought of it as women's rights then—had, in some measure, earned his respect.

The incident had secured my job. I now had the upper hand. I really did not want to leave the company. I wouldn't have to announce any change to the family, the awkward questions would have been so hard to answer. I decided to gamble. I sent my regrets to the other firm.

He kept his word.

I had a postcard from Ingrid from the north. There was a sad quote from Oscar Wilde and scribbled underneath, "Do hearts ever truly mend?" So Carl had gone. I placed her grief in my own heart and carried it with me, carefully, like a hurt bird.

Soon after that, the accountant came to my room one morning with a book in his hand. My heart sank. However, it proved to be a copy of Oliver Twist, handsomely bound in green leather lettered in gold. He said he had a whole set of Dickens and he wondered if I would like to have it as his wife was preparing for repatriation and they were clearing out some of their things. It seemed a pity to send a set like that to the secondhand dealers if there was someone who would appreciate and cherish it. He knew I liked good books, he added.

How he knew that I couldn't say, but it was a far cry from Frank Harris and his life and loves, and I accepted the gesture with good grace. He brought the entire set, I took them home book by book, and both my mother and I feasted on Dickens for many months. Her reading had improved far ahead of her speech. Good books were expensive and hard to come by and I treasured all those I had.

One day George asked me if I would come to dinner at the apartment where he lived with his parents. I had met his father very briefly at the Shanghai Cricket Club earlier in the summer though I had had no chance to get to know him in the throes of the match, but I had never met his mother. My parents were doubtful, I had never been allowed to visit a young man at his residence before, but they took George's word when he assured them that his parents would indeed be present for the entire evening.

So, with that obstacle overcome, we start out for the apartment on Rue du Consulat. On the way in the bus I learn that in addition to the sister I met at the Cricket Club George also has two older brothers who emigrated to Canada and a younger brother who lives with them in the apartment.

I have never asked George about his family, but he now tells me that his father is an architect and worked for the Customs, but that he lost his job when the British handed the Customs back to the Chinese and has not been able to get another because of the Depression.

I do not know that there has been a Depression. My father

has worked at the same job for sixteen years and I never knew about the Depression. We have always been depressed more or less. But I don't tell George that. The way he speaks of it I know it should be in capital letters and that it must have been something serious. I suppose we have been very lucky, all the men in our family retained their jobs throughout the period he refers to. If anything, our position has bettered itself over the past few years. I understand that George has to pay quite a large share of his salary toward the apartment and his board.

I am surprised to discover an English family that is not rich. I now realize as the bus chugs on that I have never given a thought to George's family, nor to the families of any of the swains. It seems to me that I never seriously thought of them as having homes or families at all. They could just have been around for my entertainment. Perhaps this odd vision of the young men in my life was due to the fact that up to now I have been allowed to visit only my girlfriends. This restriction has deprived the young men of depth in my mind, made them seem like images passing by on a screen rather than real people. I think of a young man with sloping shoulders and a long neck whom Grace Arlington and I called "The Bottle" and how we used to giggle and cross streets to avoid him. We never thought of him as a real person with feelings that could be hurt.

George also tells me about his mother. She came out to China as a nurse but gave up nursing during her five pregnancies. Since the Depression she has been trying to shore up the family finances in various ways, from making and selling chocolates to running a kindergarten. His mother has had a rough time over the past few years, George says.

We arrive at an old building on Rue du Consulat, and take the elevator to the fourth floor. The elevator is operated by an aged and very sleepy Chinese, and is built like a cage with all its innards visible. As we are slowly hauled up I watch the cables anxiously.

The apartment is not very large, not like Nina's apartment, and it's much more crowded than our Victory Terrace house. I see at a glance that the furniture is not elegant, nothing like my Aunt Lena's blue-velvet sitting-room with the pictures in gold frames.

I like both his parents at once. His father is welcoming and genial, now that he is not involved in the organization of a cricket match. I soon discover that he is very knowledgeable. This puts me on my guard but he makes no demands on me and I gradually relax. His mother is affable, a small, sharp-featured woman with a wry sense of humour, who holds herself erect and speaks in a clipped, authoritative but unthreatening manner. She is obviously very fond of her husband and allows him to pretend that he is the king of the castle whereas in actuality I think they both know that she is the rock on which this castle stands.

I am told that George's sister has gone to England. She has gone to marry Julian of the flowing hair and heart-stopping mien, whose parents sent him out of the country earlier to save him from this disastrous involvement. I can imagine how shaken they will be when they discover she has followed him. George's parents are very proud of their daughter, of her talent and independence and her determination. I remember our talk at the Cricket Club and I wonder if, in spite of their geniality, they might take exception to me because I am trapped by the Anglican Church and have not established myself as a free thinker. I discover that, contrary to other British people I know, they have a great interest in the Soviet Union. They do not hold it against me that my parents are emigrants.

At this particular moment in time George's parents are dismayed by the Treaty of Friendship signed between the Russians and the Germans. They championed the Revolution when it happened, deplored the Intervention. They still believe that the Russian Revolution will bring about the long-awaited social changes the world has been waiting for.

They are alarmed by Russia's pact with Germany. I can see that this pact has created a conflict of loyalties for them.

In the meantime the Chinese boy is serving us dinner. We are to have a great English delicacy, brains. When I discover this I think I might throw up. The brains, fried in bread crumbs, are really quite tasty, but I refuse a second helping, rather too quickly for true politeness. We have an English pudding for dessert. The pudding is heavy and smells faintly of sweat. I smother it in golden syrup but I don't like the golden syrup either. I hope I'm not asked to dinner too often.

On the whole, despite the brains and the pudding, the evening is a great success and George brings me home exactly on time.

The fall drags on with depressing news from the front. In November we hear that my Aunt Lena, the doctor and Nina, far away in Europe, have managed to secure passages on a ship and will leave Europe at the end of the month. If all goes well they will be home for Christmas.

George is now dividing his time between his new job at the Shanghai Gas Company and his duty on the ships at night. A depression hangs over the city, so many of our friends have left, the Y is no longer the place it used to be, no-one has any heart for debates. We try to counter this gloom with our youth and our optimism. One day we discover the Borisoff concerts.

Since the Great Rift, my Uncle Ernest and Maria Mikhailovna have been living on the top floor of a house owned by a couple called Borisoff. They live there with their two Alsatians whose advent had been the final straw precipitating the rift, and Mother and I visit them occasionally. My father, having become the recluse my mother bemoans, never accompanies us on these visits. Though we have been there a number of times it is a while before I discover the treasure hidden in the lower rooms of the house, the rooms that the Borisoffs occupy themselves.

On one of our visits my mother and I meet the Borisoffs who have also been invited to dinner. It is a somewhat frenzied affair with the guests slipping on scatter-rugs strewn strategically over the stains on the floor, Maria Mikhailovna lobbing plates of food over the heads of the slavering, leaping, ill-disciplined dogs, and the beleaguered Chinese help scurrying frantically between dining-room and kitchen bearing haphazard offerings. At the end of the meal, during a lull in the hubbub, Mrs. Borisoff, possibly with a view to escape, asks me if I like music and then, without waiting for a reply, hustles me out of the room and down the stairs. She wants to show me something, she says. She throws open the door to her suite and I find myself face to face with the treasure.

The treasure comprises thousands of records.

The records, all of classical music, are ranged around the rooms on shelves extending from floor to ceiling.

Mrs. Borisoff tells me that the records number over seven thousand and that her husband holds concerts every Friday. If I'd like to come and perhaps bring a friend, we would be very welcome. I say I know just the friend to bring.

George and I start to go to the Borisoff concerts every Friday. Mr. Borisoff starts the evening off with a talk on the music we are going to hear, first in Russian, then in English. We listen to the music, made so much more pleasurable by his knowledgeable interpretations, and at the end of the concert Mrs. Borisoff serves refreshments. I never realized there was so much to know about music. I am totally enchanted. Mr. Borisoff, in his eagerness to share the great passion in his heart, has opened a whole new world to me.

Week after week George and I walk through the streets of the French Concession with its exclusive homes set in large gardens surrounded by walls or tall hedges and great protective trees to the home of the Borisoffs. At first we walk to the sound of crunching autumn leaves scattered thickly underfoot, then we walk warmly bundled up against the winter winds, and when we have walked our way through fall and winter, we are rewarded by the first soft nights of spring. And week after week the bond between us strengthens and grows warmer and sweeter to the strains of Bach and Tchaikovsky and Beethoven, until we can no longer remember a time when we have not been together, when we have not known each other. And one night under the bursting blossoms of an old magnolia tree, with the eastern moon our only witness, George gathers up the courage to kiss me. I do not dodge this kiss, he has been wise not to be precipitant, unlike the ardent Quaker. I am a woman to be wooed, not hustled.

The war rumbles on in Europe. My father is always at the radio when I come home in the evenings, listening to the late news. George takes to staying for a cup of tea and a cookie, and when my parents have gone up to bed we cosy up on the sofa and allow the radio to burble on softly. The war recedes during those precious hours and we have no thought for anything but each other. It doesn't seem to matter, after all, that the USSR is forcing Estonia to side with the Germans.

Spring changes to summer, and while the Germans invade Holland and Belgium and Luxemburg, while Mr. Chamberlain suffers through his resignation and Mr. Churchill forms his Coalition, and while the Dunkirk evacuation is taking place, I continue to work for the pharmaceutical company, where the staff is now curbing all amorous inclinations, and to play tennis at the Race Course, and George continues to play cricket at the Shanghai Cricket Club, to work at the Shanghai Gas Company and to do duty on the ships at night. In June, when the USSR issues an ultimatum to the Baltic States and forms new governments, my father enters into a period of even deeper depression. He loses weight and gets into the habit of hitching up his pants rather than have the extra hole put into his belt. It just seems too much trouble to take it to a shop for alterations.

Deep troughs appear down the sides of his face. His jowls hang loosely. When the Battle of Britain opens, George achieves a measure of fame by scoring magnificently for his team, The Shanghai Wanderers, and his name shows up in headlines two inches tall. The war comes out second in newsworthiness that day.

Our courtship is so gradual that when George one evening formally asks my father for his permission to marry me, it is by way of an anticlimax. My parents are now so fond of him there is no question about him in their minds. My father rises above his depression, opens a bottle of wine reserved for New Year celebrations, and we toast the occasion. My mother smiles enigmatically as we talk of the uncertain future. Just keep him guessing, she seems to say.

Chapter Nine

We were to become formally engaged on my birthday, 2 October. Though I wanted the day to be perfect, it was beleaguered with problems. A week or so earlier my mother, preparing a mutton roast for the oven, pricked her finger with a sliver from the bone. Soon she was fighting for her life.

There was no medication for blood poisoning. My doctor uncle prescribed constant hot-water baths for the swollen arm. Aunt Lida came to live with us and ministered to my mother. The doctor looked exceedingly grave and I was devastated. The old nagging fear that God was punishing me surfaced, but my mother was suffering more than I was and she too had looked forward to this day. It didn't make sense. I was sick with worry.

Though the doctor had sounded a lot more hopeful the

night before my birthday, the day started out badly. Nobody remembered that it was my birthday. When I got to the office I heard that a typhoon warning had gone out. At mid-day the wind began to blow and a torrential downpour darkened the windows. Soon the wind had risen to full typhoon velocity. The office was closed down and I struggled to Nanking Road against the gale only to find the central area of downtown flooded. There was no transportation, every rickshaw had a fare, the trams and buses had stopped running. The only place I could think of that was within walking distance was George's apartment.

I set off down the Bund. The water rose to my ankles, then to my calves, then to my knees. I bundled my frock up around my thighs and ploughed on. It wasn't very cold, but I knew the dangers of the flood waters. They came up from the sewers.

At George's apartment the elevator man shook his head as he took me up. I didn't know whether his concern was for me or for his floor, which I was rapidly converting into a miniature lake.

Luckily George's mother was home. She ran a hot bath and warned me to wash my legs first and then change the water for the rest of my bath. Although I could see my tale alarmed her, the cheerful, brisk, unflappable British nurse surfaced. We set my shoes by the stove in the kitchen in which a casserole of bubble and squeak was cooking.

The typhoon intensified. I knew I would never get home, I would have to stay the night.

I phoned home to explain my predicament. I spoke to my aunt as my mother was too ill. My aunt was shocked. There had to be a way to get home, she said. Under no circumstances was I to stay at my fiancé's home for the night. Did I care nothing for my reputation? What did I expect her to tell my mother? Didn't I realize that my mother was close to death?

Fortunately my father had managed to get home on one of

the last buses and came to an amicable agreement with George's mother, but I knew that through no fault of my own, I had upset both my aunt and my sick mother.

That evening, after supper, George gave me my engagement ring but I could scarcely keep back my tears.

When I got home the next day I was devastated by my aunt's reception of me. Everyone else had managed to get home, she said, how was it that I had got caught? There would be gossip about me now, she said, servants carried tales, I had caused my mother anxiety and grief. The fact that I had walked through sewage did not impress her.

My mother was too ill to say much, but I knew that even though she was fighting for her life, she was truly worried about my reputation. I was shocked. I had not realized just how relentless a hold these mores had upon my family. I thought of the amorous staff at the office and thanked God I had handled the matter myself.

With the aid of my good aunt's devoted and tireless care, my mother recovered. But the day I had wanted to be the most perfect in my life had turned out a total disaster.

With my mother's recovery both she and my aunt relented and by the time Christmas rolled around we were all on good terms again, but I never quite overcame my hurt at the unfair way I had been faulted, and my craving for freedom from the restrictive watchfulness around me intensified.

In the spring, George's parents prepared to go to Canada to join their two older sons already there. As soon as we got married, they said, we could follow and George could enlist in the Canadian forces.

That we might emigrate to Canada so that George could join up had never even occurred to me. At first I was appalled, but when I saw his quiet acceptance of the fact that this was the only thing for him to do, I rallied. However, I could see that this plan dismayed my parents by the very fact that they said so little about it. They had already parted from their beloved older daughter. I hugged my father and assured him that the moment I set foot in Canada I would start immigration proceedings for him and Mother, but this did not inspire him to enthusiasm. I overlooked the fact that at 68 another uprooting could well be viewed by him only with despair.

But I had another worry. Marrying an Englishman did not change the fact that I was still basically an undesirable enemy subject, and as such could be a major stumbling block to George's acceptance by the Canadian government. Our marriage plans might well founder.

While the war raged through Greece and Yugoslavia and northern Africa, George's parents packed. We saw them off at the docks. The thick brown waters swirled below us and we said goodbye to them to the cacophony of tooting vessels, creaking machinery, thudding packing-cases and the soul-racking songs of the coolies. They were leaving behind them 30-odd years of life in the Far East. They said nothing about how they felt.

In spite of my fears we started to make plans for our wedding and arrange finances for our forthcoming departure. George refused to consider my apprehensions in regard to my enemy status. Once I was his wife I would be British. But I feared this optimistic view might not be that of a government at war. Then on 22 June we woke to the news that the German army had invaded Russia. A titanic struggle had begun, demonic forces had been let loose, but my only thought was one of relief. At last I was on the right side! There was nothing to hinder our marriage now, nothing to stop our immigration.

We had decided on 10 July for our wedding day. It would be a late-afternoon wedding and Aunt Lena offered her home for the reception, as she had done for my sister, so long ago it now seemed. I remembered how my bridesmaid's dress of champagne-beige had been the first new dress of my life, how I had been given silk stockings to wear for the first time and how these had been withdrawn for any but truly state occasions.

Invitations were sent out. These everyone accepted except the Sokoloffs. The Sokoloffs declined.

This declination reflected an interesting split in the Russian emigrant community. When the war started many Russian emigrants sided with the Germans, and indeed they had little cause to love the British. Later, when the Germans began to batter away at their homeland, some of the Russians turned against the Germans, a Russian pride deeper than political expediency was at work, but some still hoped that if the Germans broke the power of the Bolsheviks the monarchy might be restored. They were torn, confused people. In addition I felt I myself may have been to blame in part for the Sokoloffs' refusal to attend my wedding, as I had somewhat drifted away from Olga, but whatever the reason I was shocked and saddened, and even though the wedding arrangements were pressing I spent a great deal of time pondering the fragility of people's emotions and how dangerous it was to take goodwill for granted.

On a different note I heard from Ingrid. There were congratulations, messages of hope and well-wishing, and beneath the cheer, a tearing sadness.

Nina was to be my chief bridesmaid and I asked two other girls with whom I had become involved at the Y to make up a charming trio.

So while the Russians were being slaughtered across a battlefront of 1800 miles we put the finishing touches to the wedding preparations. I had spent hours agonizing over dress patterns suggested to me by my Aunt Lida and she and my mother had been cutting and fitting lengths of material and twirling the wheel of the ancient machine for weeks. While regiments perished in Africa I argued about my bouquet and sat in on plans for the wedding buffet with my Aunt Lena who was in charge of refreshments. And in the middle of all this activity, just as at the time of my confirmation, I was once again suddenly beset by doubts and guilt.

My early revolt against the beliefs of the church had not been eradicated by the gentle manipulations of the Reverend Ottewell, my lost faith had not been restored by the weekly utterances of the august Dean of the Cathedral, nor by the expectations of my parents. In my mind I had no business having a church wedding. But against these efforts at logical and honest thought, there still rose the towering edifice of organized religion. Even George, the non-conformist, saw the need to acquiesce to my family's expectations. I didn't stand a chance. Organized religion won hands down.

Because I was such a favourite of theirs due to my fly-paper memory that had enabled me to spout hundreds of Biblical texts over the years, both the Dean and the Reverend Ottewell officiated at the wedding ceremony. The huge Cathedral dwarfed the small wedding party of 50 or 60 people. My bridesmaids, in pink-and-blue-and-green were like a bouquet of exquisite flowers. My own dress, made of the flimsiest georgette, for it was the hottest time of the year, was glorified by a pair of enormous bishop sleeves, caught up at the wrists and falling in delicate folds over my hands—long sleeves being mandatory for the bride at an Anglican wedding. I was enchanted with them. They were my aunt's creation.

We knelt at the altar rail, agnostic couple that we were, on the hottest day of the year, receiving the blessings of the church, endlessly it seemed, and all I was aware of was the streams of perspiration rolling down my body and my arms and soaking into the carpet beneath me. By the end of the service I was drenched right down to the cuffs of my splendid bishop sleeves.

At my aunt's house an impressive reception awaited us. My aunt had spent hours making dozens of piroshkee, those inimitable Russian pastries with delectable fillings, and had arranged for an abundance of other food in accordance with the tenets of Russian hospitality, and champagne corks were popping.

The outer ring of emigrant adults whose influence I was so eager to shed, were well represented at the reception. Included among them and dressed grandly in his tuxedo was the deadly-eyed dentist, then in the throes of the bee-keeping brainstorm, and with him, flute-voiced as ever, the faithful and resilient Tanya. Dr. Gerber was there, nervously fingering an appetizer, unable to decide whether to eat it or not, and the Rezzinis, standing sedately side by side, like two full-bosomed thrushes, holding their champagne glasses, she with her exquisite pearls draped round her neck, he looking pleased and pompous, with no intimations yet of the breach that would affront his peers. The stout and influential Mr. Lazaridy, distiller par excellence of the famous Lazaridy vodkas, leaned, puffing, by an open window, attended by his smiling, nodding wife. They had arranged passages for us on a ship to Tsingtao where we were to spend our honeymoon. Travel accommodation was getting very tight as one by one the ships were commandeered for the war effort—we were lucky to have friends with pull.

Meeting head on with the emigrants and not a little bewildered by the magnificent spread my aunt had prepared, were the foreign members of both my office staff and George's, mostly British, a handful of English friends who were still in the city, the Reverend Ottewell and the lordly Dean of the Anglican Cathedral. These last two eminent gentlemen had welcomed us joyously to the altar thinking that they had safely enfolded me once again in the bosom of the church and persuaded George to forgo his foolish views. I half-wished it were true, conformity is so comfortable.

After the reception all those who cared to dance were invited to the roof garden of the swish French Club. My dress was still damp from the ceremony at the sweltering Cathedral and under the magical eastern stars I suddenly realized that my glorious bishop sleeves were undergoing an alarming change. By the time we got home they had shrunk to elbow-length.

We did not consummate our marriage that night. I was exhausted and I felt extremely unwell. The next morning I awoke with what was surely the worst cold of the century. But we were leaving on our honeymoon the following day, our passages were paid for, there could be no delay. I spent the day in bed, blowing my nose and groaning, while George packed.

We went to Tsingtao. I had always wanted to go to Tsingtao, I had heard so much about it. Tsingtao had originally been colonized by German settlers and their forts were still there, abandoned, overgrown with grass and weeds, desolate. There was the famous lighthouse, nicknamed Moaning Minnie, there were the yellow sands, bountifully flung in elegant crescents, the extravagant stretch of water rolling to Japan, the gentle hills and woods. It was all there, just as it had been described to me.

This year, however, there was something more, something vaguely ominous. On a beach that had up to that time been used exclusively by white people, as had the beaches in most holiday resorts in China, there were Japanese soldiers.

They were not in uniform, they were on holiday. It was later that we learned they were army men. They lay on the sands clad in G-strings, and they splashed and swam in waters previously reserved only for whites. There were no Japanese women. We left the main beach and went elsewhere. Although we had long been aware of the Japanese infiltration into China, and more especially since the 1937 carnage, this confrontation was singularly disturbing.

But apart from this minatory presence, our honeymoon was idyllic. We stayed at a small rural hotel and had our meals on a wide, ramshackle verandah. My ignorance of sex was not a stumbling block to our lovemaking. My handsome young husband proved to be wise and patient and though the contraceptives we used were primitive, especially a triangular-shaped cake, breath-stoppingly caustic, we accepted discomforts and failures with equanimity and good humour, and, possibly because of them, savoured successes and pleasures with special delight. And we loved each other very, very much.

We visited the abandoned forts and we went into the small town back of the resort and wandered through its simple streets and stores, hand in hand. We walked in the hills and woods and I learned to ride a bicycle, a childhood ambition long denied, and in the evenings we danced at a local night club and spent long hours walking under the stars and talking about our imminent departure for Canada. With the curious optimism of the young we skirted the dangers attendant upon George's intention to join the Canadian forces and spoke only of how pleasant life would be in Canada when the war was over. We persuaded ourselves that it could not last long.

At the end of our walks we would creep across the creaking boards of the hotel verandah to our room anxious to wake no-one, for we were still shy of our new status, and I was conscious of the cry of pain I had let go on our first night and that I was convinced had been heard by every Tsingtao resident for miles around.

So it was with regret that we finally boarded a ship back home. I was approaching the end of my life in China. In a month or two I would be on another ship, bound for Canada. We arrived to the news that the Japanese had landed forces in Indo-China, nobody knew to what purpose. We remembered the forebodings we had felt in Tsingtao on the beach.

We returned to Victory Terrace. My mother had sacrificed her large upstairs bedroom for us and had made it pretty with new drapes and flowers. She wanted to make my last days with them pleasant. But I was already moving away from this ambience. Since I knew emigration was inevitable, I had been gradually adapting to the idea of leaving, much as I had adapted to my exiled life in Hong Kong. Although it had come in so strange and sad a guise, this had to be the opportunity to attain that freedom I had craved ever since I returned from Hong Kong, the freedom from the rings of adults that hemmed me in. In spite of the unspoken sorrow of my parents and my fears for George, I knew in my secret heart that starting a new life that George and I could shape ourselves was what I wanted above all else. I could not disguise this desire and I had to make the best of the unfavourable circumstances of its fulfilment.

Shortly after our return George went to arrange for our passages to Canada. He discovered that the Canadian "Empress" ships had been taken off the Shanghai-Vancouver run to be transformed into troopships. All direct sailing connections between Shanghai and Vancouver had been discontinued. Our only hope lay in the American President Lines sailing to San Francisco, and to complicate matters further they informed us that they would require the presentation of our immigration papers before they would sell us any tickets.

We had no immigration papers.

George visited the Canadian Trade Commissioner. A series of cables passed between George and his parents. Ottawa agreed to send the necessary documents, but we would have to wait.

We both returned to work. Day after day passed. The blue implacable skies were curiously oppressive. Their silent vault seemed to hold back some revelation. We waited. George visited the Trade Commissioner again. Though the Commissioner knew there would be no problem with our immigration he did not have the authority to provide the necessary papers and the shipping line would not accept his verbal assurances. Every day we searched the hall table for mail the moment we came through the door. Day after day there was nothing from Canada. We couldn't understand it.

The stress of this waiting period was somewhat alleviated

by a newcomer to the scene in the person of a Greek gentle-man, an aspirant to Nina's hand in marriage, whom I shall call Dino. My cousin had become involved with the racing crowd in the city and in the cooler fall weather we had all attended the races, betting our twopence-worth on the sprightly Mongolian ponies. In this rarefied circle of horse owners Nina had met Dino. He had fallen like a duck shot through the heart.

Dino was older than Nina, but attractive, generous and extremely wealthy. Nina wasn't sure of her feelings. She vacillated and the see-sawing romance helped to take our minds off our own uncertainties, and the growing horror of the war.

While Mr. Churchill and Mr. Roosevelt worked out the idyllic text of the Atlantic Charter, Dino wined and dined Nina. While the Persian Shah bowed out, he planned treats for all of us driving us in his flashy car, always the host. While the Germans occupied Kiev, Dino purchased horses and gave us racing tips. While they battered at Moscow we watched the gay whirl of Dino's courtship. But all the while at the back of our minds we were waiting.

I bought long underwear for the freezing winters I was told to expect in Canada. I bought a wonderful golden-brown fur coat. I avoided the desolate look in my father's eyes. Were we not all going to be reunited as soon as the war was over, perhaps sooner? Day after day we waited.

And at last one day the mail brought the long-awaited envelope. The papers had been sent by sea mail. It had taken such an age, they must have come on a freighter round the Cape of Good Hope! It was a wonder they had arrived at all.

Hopes riding high we booked passages on the first avail-able steamer, the USS President Harrison. It was to sail in the middle of December. I blocked out my father's bleak query—"Just before Christmas?"

At the end of November we began to pack. We had two large cabin trunks and a variety of suitcases. Ah Foh and a friend lugged the trunks up to our bedrooms. They stood with their lids open, waiting to swallow our belongings, to snap their locks in the face of our past.

And then, early in December, we heard that the USS President Harrison would not be coming to Shanghai after all. It had been detained at Manila. No reasons were given. If we wanted to board it we would have to catch it at Manila.

A familiar foreboding filled us. It was the same foreboding we had felt on the beach at Tsingtao in the presence of the G-stringed Japanese soldiers, the same uneasiness that had surfaced when we heard that the Japanese had landed forces in Indo-China. George began to negotiate for passages to Manila. We stepped up our packing.

On 8 December I was wakened at sunrise from a deep sleep. I had no idea what had wakened me except that it was something quite unusual, but as I came to more fully I knew it had been a deep and distantly thunderous vibration. As I listened, suddenly afraid for I was at once reminded of 1937, it came again. I leapt out of bed and rushed to the window, pulling aside the new drapes. My sudden movement wakened George as the explosions had not, and at the same moment I heard my mother calling from her upstairs bedroom. I ran up.

Mother was out on the little roof garden in her wrap in the biting December morning, staring up at the sky. I too looked up and saw an unforgettable sight. I saw a rainbow stretching across the pale blue winter sky, just wakened to colour, and against the sky I saw small black planes crisscrossing each other, diving and shooting upwards, and upon each dive leaving behind a scattering of what looked like leaves twirling and glittering in the morning sun. As these fell we identified them as pamphlets. Some fell on our roof garden and we stared at them, immobilized, unable to reach out and touch them. We stood there, shivering in our wraps, uncomprehending.

George had been listening to the radio and now he too

hurried up the stairs, followed by my father and Ah Foh.

"It's a Japanese strike," George said. "They've taken over the Settlement. I can't get anything but bulletins from the Japanese headquarters. Come and listen."

We followed him down and listened, while Ah Foh brought down the leaflets from the roof garden and pored over them, his ivory skin a strange grey. The Chinese were terrified of the Japanese and with good reason.

On the radio a calm voice told us not to panic. It told us that the Japanese Imperial Forces had taken over the city of Shanghai. It told us to carry on our business as usual and that we would be informed periodically of the procedures that were taking place. Directives would be issued from time to time. We were requested to follow these and warned to co-operate in full. We were warned not to try to leave the city.

We turned the radio dial feverishly to see if other stations had something else to tell us, but the reports were the same everywhere. There was no outside news.

My mother asked Ah Foh what the pamphlets said.

Ah Foh, who had learned the basics of reading and writing since he had come to the big city, was ready with his information. "Paper say Japanese good. Say Japanese help Chinese people. Not tlue, Missy. Japanese no good. Me no likee."

"Me no likee too, Ah Foh," Mother said helplessly.

My mother looked from face to face, her own full of distress. She appealed to my father. "You won't go out, will you?"

"But I must," my father said. Except for a few days of illness and the 1937 restrictions imposed on the whole city, my father had never missed a day of work. It was unthinkable that a mere invasion by some Japanese soldiers should stop him. "We must all go," he said. His face was grave and the twitch had appeared in his cheek. "Maybe not you though," he said to me.

Indignantly I cried, "But of course I'm going. Why should *I* stay at home? Do you think they'll cut off our heads the moment we step outside?" Nobody answered me.

After a breakfast for which I had lost my appetite, I left the house at my usual time. In the streets there were Japanese soldiers posted at every major intersection. They stood there with their feet apart, their bayonets ready, and no-one was permitted to walk on the sidewalk anywhere near them. I discovered later that this was because they were representatives of the Emperor, which made the space around them sacred and inviolable. They made this clear by grunting at anyone who came too close, and poking them with their rifle butts.

I stood at the bus stop and watched the blind Chinese beggar for whom my mother always had some coppers, making for the soldier at the crossing. He was tapping his cane, rattling the coppers in his bowl, oblivious of the momentous events that were taking place around him. He came straight at the Japanese soldier. Periodically he lifted his blind eyes to the sky and uttered a forlorn cry. When he was within arm's length of the soldier he was swept aside. I heard what sounded like an oath delivered by the soldier. The beggar stumbled and fell, ignorant of what had struck him. The soldier kicked him with his army boot. He kicked him again and again until the beggar collapsed in the gutter. Then the soldier laughed. The other Chinese hurried by, eyes downcast, no-one stopped to help the beggar. He lay still now, his forlorn cry silenced.

My cavalier attitude of the morning wilted. Impotent rage filled my chest like a large foreign body, but there was nothing I could do either. I was afraid. I climbed aboard my bus.

On the bus people were talking. Information had seeped through in spite of the news blackout on the air. I now learned that what had wakened me had been the bombing of the British and American gunboats in the harbour by the

Japanese. They had been sunk. There had also been a huge strike somewhere in a place called Pearl Harbour in Hawaii. The Japanese had entered the war against the Allies. A numbness crept over me. There would be no emigration to Canada.

At the office I found the boss and the accountant busy stuffing papers up the chimney of the fireplace in the boss' office. They were company papers and they were hiding them before the Japanese came to take over the firm as they were bound to do. I never found out exactly what it was they were trying to hide from the Japanese and I really didn't care. For all I knew it could have been the *Life and Loves of Frank Harris* and his various confreres in the literary world. Actually I believe they were trying to hide the formulas for the medications that Mr. Boukoff so mysteriously concocted below stairs. But I wasn't registering much. I was just too dumbfounded by the stunning end to all our plans.

Chapter Ten

My mother and I are hurrying home. We have been gossiping over tea at my aunt's house and are late for supper. Just as we approach Victory Terrace we hear shrill whistles. There is a commotion. People are running. Two policemen race to the crossroads and rope off our street. We, and a crowd of others, are caught behind the barricade.

It is the Pao Chia. The Pao Chia are Chinese puppet policemen trained by the Japanese to simulate procedures following upon an aerial attack. A section of the city is roped off, the place where a bomb has supposedly fallen, and all traffic is halted. Sometimes we have to stay where we are for hours. It is power; the Pao Chia enjoy that power. Only yesterday a woman in the throes of labour pains was denied access to a hospital just on the other side of the Pao Chia rope.

Mother and I look around for an escape. We see a small lane we know that leads to the back of our terrace. We sneak around the crowd and into the lane. For once we have outwitted the Pao Chia.

This evening, in our Vancouver home, in the latitudinarian eighties, we sit in front of the fire and talk about that morning when our lives changed so dramatically. It is Thanksgiving and I am serving little goodies to go with the after-dinner coffee and tea.

Thanksgiving is my favourite festival. "It seems we can never be thankful enough to have got out of all that mess alive," I say.

"Only just," my aunt reminds us. "And not all of us did."

She is remembering her dear husband and my father. But I can't help thinking that their spirits are somehow with us, that they are glad to see us all sitting here together, comfortable and at peace.

"We were planning to go to Canada," I recall.

"Maybe it was better the way it turned out," says my aunt. "You might have lost George if you'd gone."

I remember how imperative it had seemed to both of us to leave. How George knew his duty lay overseas and I knew I had to go too, that my life was somehow ineluctably bonded to his. How we had been sure, with the unbounded optimism of youth, that he would survive, that the war would be over soon—in Shanghai it was hard to believe that a world war was actually raging. I recall the sadness in my father's eyes and my reassurances that our separation would not be for long. And always at the back of my mind had been that secret desire for independence. If I went first to Canada, I thought, my relationship with those of the family who wanted to follow would be different. I would set up values of my own, their mores would no longer be mine. I would be my own mistress. I would truly have my own corner as my mother had told me so long ago every person should have.

"It was fate that you didn't go," my aunt says. Her firm belief in fate never wavers.

"Fate in the shape of Japanese aggression," I laugh.

"God arranges things in His own way," she says, rebuking my levity.

I put my arm around her as she snuggles into her favourite corner of my chesterfield. We share a poignancy of memory that is almost unbearable at times, it is ingrained so deeply, it has made such ineradicable inroads into the psyche. Our life in the Orient was a life lived on an island briefly set aside by time, a life that in some way lived on itself, left out of the convolutions of world currents. Everyone believed that the Shanghai way of living would go on forever. And when those convolutions caught up with us, we were incredulous.

My sister, writing once from New Zealand, recalled how painful it had been to live there in Shanghai among all that misery and know you were powerless to help, that the problem was too vast. It was a familiar feeling to all of us, and because we knew we were powerless we tried to shut it out. We bobbed along on the surface but the poignancy of what was the real essence of China ate into us in spite of ourselves, and when I longed to escape I did not know that I would carry that poignancy with me wherever I went, woven for all time into the texture of my soul, an emotion so strong that it made a place like Vancouver seem like a picture postcard, spectacular, but somehow only two-dimensional.

There is chatter in the room but my aunt and I sit in our corner and stare into the fire while a series of scenes passes through my mind.

Shanghai has become one huge internment camp. It is surrounded by the Japanese army and no-one is allowed to enter or to leave without permits. Enemy nationals are not allowed to leave at all. I see us standing in long queues to register. We are given red armbands to wear at all times, signifying our enemy status. Our bank accounts have been frozen. Private assets and property belonging to enemy nationals are slated for confiscation. We hear that civil assembly centres are being readied.

I meet a friend on the bus. Her eyes are red from weeping. Her husband has been taken away no-one knows where to. We hear that some swift arrests have been made, at random it seems at first. Then it begins to surface that the men removed are high-powered operators with huge assets, influential pressmen, or those who have been participating in anti-Japanese activities. Later we hear they have been taken to a place called Bridge House. We hear rumours of tortures, brutal disciplines, deaths.

I suddenly see Nina, indescribably lovely, in a bridal gown. She has decided to marry Dino. Dino's Far Eastern assets have been frozen by the Japanese and his ships appropriated in the harbour, but she has accepted him nonetheless. I'm glad that's settled. Everyone's been giving Nina free advice, which she's been tolerating with her usual good grace. My mother said if Nina was marrying Dino for his money she should ponder the fact that it wouldn't be his money she'd see every morning by her side. I don't think Nina's motives are anyone's business but her own, she can hardly be marrying Dino for his wealth now and in any case her own family's affluent enough. Dino's charm has won her over.

I'm at Nina's wedding. It's April and I'm the matron-of-honour. I wear a rainbow-hued taffeta gown with a pink flower in my hair. My hair has started to darken, the platinum blondness admired so much by Maria Mikhailovna, for which she said Hollywood stars would give their right arms, has long disappeared, but I fancy myself in my rainbow dress, and my head empties for a short while of anxieties and fears.

The wedding takes place in the Russian Orthodox Church and is full of pomp and ceremony and mysterious rituals. I can't take my eyes off my cousin, luminous in her gown, like the dream of all brides everywhere through decades of weddings, and I think Dino is very lucky.

The reception is held in a spacious hall. There are too many guests to accommodate in Aunt Lena's apartment. Strings have been pulled and a variety of delicacies have been procured and there is no shortage of champagne.

Shortly thereafter the Japanese authorities declare all weddings taking place after the occupation to be invalid.

Now I see myself in slacks and a shirt riding a bicycle to Nina's new apartment in the French Concession. We ride bicycles everywhere because the Japanese have requisitioned all the gasoline supplies in the city for their war effort. There are no more buses and the electricity for trams has also been limited. It takes my father forever to get to and from work. As I ride anxiety clouds my mind. Misfortune has befallen Nina. Shortly after her wedding she fell ill with typhoid fever, and although she recovered the illness has left her legs paralyzed. Even my doctor uncle is baffled.

I park and lock my bicycle, take off my clips and ride the elevator up to her apartment. The apartment is elegantly appointed and her many fine wedding gifts are arranged tastefully. But Nina herself is pale and wasted. Typically, she doesn't talk about herself but about the occupation and whether we have heard anything in regard to our own possible future. I tell her all the news. According to reports the preparation of concentration camps is progressing, food is being rationed and hoarded, Chinese money is devaluating daily. My mother and Ah Foh are buying up as much grain and canned goods as they can get. All the utilities have been taken over by the Japanese although the foreign staffs are being kept on temporarily. Maria Mikhailovna is not at all well. She has had a cold and her cough is much worse. Neither of us mention a certain dread word though we both know Maria Mikhailovna's illness is not a cold. I recount our Pao Chia experience and make Nina laugh.

On the way home, Nina's illness underlines my own vulnerability to disease, bodily impairment and even death. I'm also very much afraid of getting pregnant and have stocked up on the fearful triangular contraceptives, suffering burning nights of love. I don't trust George's safes as my father has told me privately that that was how I came into the world in the first place—through a faulty safe.

One day when I turn into Kiangse Road on my way to the office, which has not yet been taken over by the Japanese, I see that all the refugees who have been living in disused doorways and openings between shop fronts, have disappeared. They have vanished as if an enormous giant with an outsize broom has swept them all away together with their lice-ridden mats and ramshackle shelters. I learn that it is part of the Japanese health drive. The refugees with their lice were the prime cause of the typhus epidemic in the city. I try not to think of what might have happened to all those unhappy people.

With inexorable efficiency the Japanese have set about inoculating the whole population of Shanghai against cholera. We have always had cholera shots, administered by my uncle, but now every resident, white and Chinese, is to have a cholera shot and to carry cholera passes on their persons at all times. Random searches are the order of the day and anyone caught without a pass is inoculated on the spot by a mobile team.

Entrepreneurial Chinese present themselves for multiple shots at various centres and sell passes to those who are afraid of needles. One over-zealous enterpriser dies and the game takes a quick down-turn.

George is playing baseball with the Japanese. The Japanese organize teams within the utility companies and pitch them one against the other. Japanese appropriators and enemy nationals play side by side on the same team. I go to watch them. The Japanese play fairly and there are no problems. I can't understand how these people can be the authors of the rumoured atrocities at Bridge House. It doesn't even seem as if we are at war.

I see Japanese soldiers arrive at our office. They inform the boss that this is a formal takeover. We are all to leave and take with us only our personal possessions. They retain the Chinese staff. Yang's eyes double in size from fright. Mr. Tong is expressionless. I gather up my things and take a last look around my room. I have worked here for so long and won a victory over sexual harassment. The Japanese are stomping around in their boots slapping red seals on everything in the office. I say goodbye to Yang and Tong wondering what they feel at the exchange of bosses. Then I shake hands with the accountant and the assistant accountant and finally with the boss. The boss tells me that he is planning to do some work at the British Residents' Association and if I'd like another job I'm welcome to go with him.

I can't believe my luck. With the Japanese takeover prices have soared and we can always do with some extra dollars. I accept his offer and he grimaces sadly.

The British Residents' Association, or as it is more fondly called, the BRA, has always functioned on behalf of the rewarding interests of the money-rich British community. Now those interests have changed. There are Britishers in need. It's a turnabout. The BRA, under the auspices of the Swiss Red Cross, will conduct a dialogue with the Japanese on matters concerning the treatment of prisoners.

At the BRA I am assigned to Bill Stewart. I am no Dr. Bookbinder but this assignment immediately strikes me as portentous, I have no idea why.

"You'll like him," says a fellow-worker on my first morning. "We all do. But I can't make head or tail of him."

I can't either at first. I see a man with a stern façade, methodical, dedicated, always busy. Tall and broad-shouldered, he is in his thirties, which seems almost elderly to me, with thinning, curly black hair, an autocratic British nose and thick-lensed glasses. I see a perfectionist, stooping over my work, scrutinizing details, neatness, exactness. I am intimidated.

Then I see the magic lantern. The taskmaster is only one of the images on the screen. There is a good genius for the needy, an ascetic who champions austerity, a fearless activist who bores through friend and foe alike, intransigent, to achieve a worthy end. And then there is the jester. The jester edges in on all those images, plays hide-and-seek, flashes in and out, on and off the screen. The jester slices through officialdom, exposes folly, undercuts conceit. No wonder my new friend is baffled. So am I.

"He's wonderful to have around," she says, bemused, "somehow nothing seems as scary when he's there."

She's right. He couldn't have come into our lives at a better time. I introduce him to George, they become friends and we form a threesome. The magic lantern throws swift images, we discover a skilled musician void of pretensions, a Britisher who treats Chinese as equals. I watch the lantern for its keystone, but its heart is never revealed. It remains closed, an enigma. The jester is its guardian. I respect that. I treasure such a secret place myself.

Life at the BRA proceeds at a clip. The Japanese never let up on new injunctions, directives, briefs. Bill Stewart, inscrutable as ever, says we should perform each task as well as we can—we might be performing it for the last time.

The friendly girl tells me that a horrid little man with a moustache, one of those ex-bosses with nothing better to do, pinched her bottom. I know who she's talking about and tell her to complain. "And lose my job?" she asks sharply. I shrug. "Thank God for decent men like Bill Stewart," she says. Yes indeed, I think.

Spring changes into summer. We no longer play tennis nor go to the races. Everything has been commandeered by the Japanese. We spend our evenings drinking tea, listening to the directives on the radio and exchanging gossip with family and friends. Nina is no better. There is no news about concentration camps. We wait.

Mr. Rezzini provides us with a temporary respite from anxiety. A bomb bursts over our staid community. Mr. Rezzini is having an affair.

His car is in evidence every evening outside the house of a woman of doubtful repute in our very own Victory Terrace.

He could have chosen some other locale, my mother says.

A mutual acquaintance has apprised my mother and my aunt of the scandal. My aunt cautions discretion. She has some influence with Mr. Rezzini, she will try to persuade him to mend his ways. Mrs. Rezzini need never know. But she reckons without the malice of the mutual acquaintance. In no time at all the juicy gossip has made the rounds of the community. Mrs. Rezzini is enlightened by a friend.

There are tears and consultations. My aunt is appointed a mediator. Mrs. Rezzini agrees to take Mr. Rezzini back if he abandons his paramour. Privately my mother declares that she would never take him back. The old goat, she says.

I recall how Mr. Rezzini smiled at the draped Venus de Milo.

I'm riding in a car in a funeral cortege. It's very hot and I'm wearing what was my wedding gown, now magically transformed by my Aunt Lida into a fashionable afternoon dress. The sleeves, elbow-length since the shrinkage disaster, are just right for the occasion and white is permissible at a summer funeral. I'm crying, mixing sweat with tears in the stuffy car.

Maria Mikhailovna has died. Her death was violent. She haemorrhaged, and before my Uncle Ernest could get a doctor she had drowned in her own blood. My Uncle Ernest is devastated.

I am not mourning Maria Mikhailovna's death as much as her life. My relatives thought her to be irresponsibly spendthrift, obsessively possessive, unforgivably passionate. She baffled them all. Our family is cool, judgmental, seldom given to emotional displays. When my mother lost her temper at that confrontation with Maria Mikhailovna it was a day to remember. Lately with the Japanese occupation and Nina's illness I have not been giving Maria Mikhailovna much thought. Although I knew of my doctor uncle's concern and of his persistent advice to her, which she as persistently ignored, I could not believe things were that bad.

But now, riding to the funeral, still in a state of shock and disbelief for Maria Mikhailovna is the first person to have died in our family, I take stock of my relationship with her. I remember the beautiful gifts she gave me when I was a child, but I also remember that it was her undisciplined generosity that had forced me out of a home I loved into one that I hated. I had felt bitter about it then. And I was deeply disturbed by the quarrels she precipitated between herself and Uncle Ernest, even drawing my parents into unwanted confrontations. But since then I have become an adult and I can view her peccadilloes with more compassion and understanding. At the time of their departure from Victory Terrace my father warned Uncle Ernest that Maria Mikhailovna was ill, that her eccentric behaviour had to be the result of a physical imbalance. He had proved to be right, but at this moment as I ride in the cortege her great obsessions and her impetuous passions ring with a kind of grandeur, proclaim a fiercer love of life than any of us seem to have, a love so intense that it blocked out the warnings of death. I mourn her life because I think she was tragically misunderstood.

One day I arrive at the BRA and find those already there in a great state. It appears that 400 people were apprehended and removed from their homes early in the morning by the Japanese gendarmerie with no reasons or destinations given distraught relatives. Rumour has it that people are being picked up all over the place. My heart drums against my ribs. Perhaps George has been picked up at his office. Perhaps I shall never see him again. No private telephone calls are allowed by the Japanese authorities at the utilities. I

132

must get to the Gas Company to see what has happened to George.

I ride my bike through the teeming traffic faster than I have ever dared ride it before. I get to the Gas Company and rush past the guard at the entrance ignoring his startled cries. Nothing has happened to George and I return to work, a trifle abashed at my panic, but later, when I get home from work I hear frightful news. Dino was one of those apprehended that morning.

I hear more details. Four Japanese gendarmes and two French policemen came to Nina's apartment early in the morning to arrest Dino. He was told to pack a suitcase. Nina begged them to tell her where they were taking Dino, explained to them that she was bed-ridden but they had paid no attention to her. After they had left with Dino six more gendarmes had arrived and had searched the apartment from top to bottom, even shaking out all the shoes. Nina had no idea what they were looking for. They had put seals on all her furniture. It was now the possession of His Imperial Majesty, the Emperor of Japan.

My mother suggests that George and I should move everything we treasure into her bedroom. If we have such a visitation there's a good chance that only our room will be sealed.

She is right. One evening, just after I come home from work we too are summoned to the front door by a great knocking. Six Japanese soldiers march into our house. My father, agitatedly, shows them his Estonian passport but they're not the slightest bit interested and wave it aside. I doubt if a single one of them has ever even heard of Estonia or cares if he has. They only want to know about George and me. We lead them upstairs to our bedroom and show them our few belongings. They put seals on all the furniture and seal the glass doors of my bookcase but by-pass my mother's bedroom. They are quite simple fellows after all, lacking my mother's shrewdness, which has saved my treasures.

133

When they have done their job they bow, click their heels and march out again. Our hearts are thumping.

It is now revealed that all the men who were arrested on that memorable morning were persons of considerable substance, suspected of having made business deals unfavourable to Japan and having engaged in inimical activities. They have all been taken to a camp in Haiphong Road. It is November, 1942.

We know our time too is approaching. Rumours are thick as mosquitoes over a swamp. We feel that we are sitting on a huge landslide that is slowly slipping away into an unknown ocean. We are trapped.

We try to comfort ourselves and one another. If the Japanese do anything truly reprehensible to us, we say, they would have to expect reprisals to their own nationals overseas. Surely that would deter them. There is such a thing as International Law, we say. We hang on to that assurance and we don't allow our innermost fears to surface. These buried fears tell us that International Law could pop like a balloon on a hot stove. Underground radios have caught and disseminated stories of deaths in Nazi concentration camps and also, and to us more immediately disturbing, brutality and atrocities in Japanese camps in other occupied zones. We have our own Bridge House already. I wonder about those baseball games.

I see my mother and myself walking home with a package of salted herring. It leaves an almost tangible odour behind us. We have been to the Estonian Consulate where we have been given the herring. Food supplies have been growing tighter daily. The Chinese currency is depreciating and prices climb. The Estonian Consulate, in conjunction with the Swiss, is able to bring in some basic staples to be distributed to Estonian nationals. I make a number of such trips to the Estonian Consulate with my mother. It is a tiny house in the French Concession now bulging with supplies. She signs papers and I help her carry their share home. The herring is smelly but ever so good.

Christmas 1942 passes, very subdued. We don't go to the German Church any more of course. The service in the Cathedral is doleful. There are black hangings around the altar. The names of the war dead from our small community are read out. There is no joy in the birth of the Child. Our New Year celebration, quietly observed at home as usual, is a little more fervent. Father tears off the calendar pages and although his face twitches a little, he manages a smile with the toast. We all respond with a kind of desperate enthusiasm, almost as if we have to put an extra spell on the coming year to counter all the bad predictions with which it is already burdened. I think of "The Death of the Old Year" and miss my sister.

Early in the New Year notices begin to be served to parties of enemy nationals informing them of impending internment. Soon after the parties disappear one by one. No-one knows where they have gone. They are told only to report at a specific place at a certain time and they are given instructions in regard to baggage. I hear that my old school has been commandeered for use as a camp. We go to see it. There is barbed wire all around it. I'm told that the plaques in the entrance hall, inscribed in gold letters year after year with the names of those who had excelled in one way or another, have been torn down and burned. Two of the plaques had my name on them. So much for fame. I know that this is one small thing I will never forgive the Japanese. I thought my name would be up in that school forever.

George is now told that his services with the Shanghai Gas Company are at an end. A Mr. Ueno takes over the books. He has been working with George for the past year. He bows and shakes George's hand. George bows back. Mr. Ueno has been a considerate and courteous enemy and he is not to blame for the war.

We wait.

The BRA is winding down. They are handing over to the

Swiss who will carry on the business of negotiating between the Japanese and the enemy nationals. They are supposed to monitor food and health facilities. What a hope, someone says. We buy canned goods. We prepare sensible clothes like the long johns I bought for Canada. We pray that we'll be interned together. Bill Stewart, straight-faced, tells us to be sure to pack a convenience for the night.

The magnolias bud, bloom, die.

We wait.